"The most rebellious thing you can do is get educated.

Forget what they told you in school. Get educated!

I ain't saying play by the rules. Get educated!

Get educated! Get educated!

Break the chains of their enslavement. Get educated!

Even if you're on the pavement. Get educated!

What a weapon that your brain is. Get educated!

Get educated! Get educated!"

AKALA

(From the album 'Knowledge Is Power')

D1509165

ONE

It was my sixth birthday when the little voice first spoke to me.

Please do understand, dear reader, that it wasn't an abstract little voice. Oh no! It belonged to a little creature who lived inside my brain. But that creature had not, up until that point, ever said a word.

That creature wasn't human. Far from it! Although its eyes were identical to my own.

If I'm to be totally honest, I must admit that I'm not exactly sure what it was. I've always just called it 'The Egot'.

The egot's skin was as red as hellfire, its hair was as bright as the midday sun, and its belly was as round as a pearl. It had webbed feet, elfish ears and lithe claws. I assumed it was male, but it could've been female; it was impossible to tell.

Yet, despite its peculiar appearance, I felt comfortable whenever I saw the egot. It possessed a powerful sort charisma which always put me at ease. It'd lift its flat cap, bend one of its spiky knees, and wink in a way which made its eye sparkle. Just seeing the egot made me feel warm and fuzzy inside.

The egot was familiar. It was a part of the scenery of my mind. My companion. My friend.

But it had never spoken. Not until the day I turned six.

I was at school when it happened, sitting at the set of desks which I shared with five other pupils. The waxy floor was illuminated by white light. The smell of pencil shavings wafted through the air.

Our teacher, Ms Brown, was standing at the front of that prefabricated space. She was scratching a tiny nub of chalk along an indifferent blackboard.

"As soon as those brave explorers stepped foot on that distant land, they were attacked by a group of wild savages," she told the class through a cloud of chalk dust.

"Ooh! Ooh!" screamed Snotty McGill.

I liked Snotty McGill. I liked all the children in my class. Back then, I think we all just tacitly assumed that we were equal. That we were all in the same boat. We didn't really think about our different genders, races or classes. We just co-existed, like one big family.

I think Snotty McGill was actually called Sarah, but we called her 'Snotty' because she always had a cold. An hour seldom passed in which she didn't either sneeze, pick her nose, or wipe a bogie onto her snot-encrusted sleeve. But she had such a lovely colour. That pink glow which comes with the flu used to engulf her like an aura. It suited her. She always looked so damn effervescent.

Anyway, as I was saying, Snotty McGill was waving her hand above her head.

"Ms! Ms!" she called. "What's a 'savage'?"

Ms Brown turned to face us. She looked chalky. Everything around her looked chalky. The floor was covered in chalk-dust and the skirting-boards were covered in chalky-ashes. Chalk residue glistened in Ms Brown's bushy hair. It coated the points of her fingers.

"Well," she said. "A savage has the body of a man, but not his civility. A savage is like an animal. He doesn't wear clothes, live in a house, study or work. He follows his base urges; to eat, drink and reproduce. But he doesn't have an intellect. He doesn't have any ambition. He's smelly, hairy and uncouth. He does the least he can to survive. And he spends most of his time sleeping or playing."

Snotty McGill looked horrified. As did Stacey Fairclough, Sleepy Sampson and Gavin Gillis. Chubby Smith looked like he was about to start a fight. Most of the class looked dumbfounded. But I felt inspired.

'*They don't have to go to school!*' I thought with envy and intrigue. '*They spend all their time playing! They sleep for as long as they like!*'

It was as if I'd stumbled across a species of super-humans. To me, the savages sounded like gods. I knew at once that I wanted to be one. I'd never been so sure of anything in my life.

The egot smiled mischievously. It rolled a whisker between its skeletal claws and tapped one of its webbed feet.

Ms Brown continued:

"Well, when the explorers stepped ashore, a pack of savages came hurtling towards them; swinging through the trees like monkeys, beating their breasts like apes, and howling like donkeys. They flocked like birds and stampeded through the dust like a herd of untamed wildebeests."

That was when the egot spoke for the first time.

It leaned up against the inside of my skull, just behind my nose, and crossed its spindly legs. Then it began to talk:

"If you want to be a savage, you should probably act like a savage. You know, you should probably stampede like a wildebeest. Maybe beat your breast like an ape. Perhaps you'd like to howl like a donkey? Yes, yes."

The egot's voice was so… so… so… So far beyond description. So subtle. So calm. So quirky. So eccentric. And so, so quiet!

The egot accentuated random letters, as if it was shocked to discover their existence. It swilled its words, like a Frenchman mulling over a glass of confused wine. And it stretched random syllables, as if it was saddened to see them go.

There was a certain melody to the egot's voice. It didn't so much speak as rhyme, like a Shakespearean actor on a crisp autumn night.

But the egot was quiet. Its voice was such a little voice. A little voice inside my head.

That little voice struck me dumb.

The egot strummed its lip, like a pensive philosopher, and waited for me to reply. But I was in a state of paralytic shock. I couldn't have replied if I'd wanted to. So the egot folded its arms, in a gesture of mock offence, and then continued on:

"I'm only telling you what you want to hear," it purred. It swirled the word 'telling' so much that the 'ell' sound reverberated five times; 'Tell-ell-ell-ell-ell-ell-ing'.

"You don't really want to succumb to civility. No, no. You want to be a savage. I think you want to jump between tables, like a monkey swinging between trees. If you thought you could get away with it, and no-one was judging you, you wouldn't think twice."

It was a moment of clarity. Bright white, unadulterated clarity. Silent. Outside of time and space.

Please do allow me to explain...

I'm a big fan of the founder of Taoism, the ancient Chinese philosopher Lao Tzu. He was a wizened old gent. His hair was as white as virgin snow and his eyes were deeper than any ocean on earth.

Well, Lao Tzu once said that 'Knowing others is wisdom. Knowing yourself is enlightenment'.

Dear reader, that's exactly how I felt! In that moment, I felt that I 'knew' myself. In that moment, I felt 'enlightened'.

Everything was clear. It was clear that I'd been living in a cage. It was clear that freedom was mine to take. It was clear what I had to do. The egot was my clarity. Everything was clear.

I remember a sense of otherworldliness, as if I'd stepped outside of the physical realm. My legs lifted my torso, my frame stood tall, and my spirit stood still. My body melted away from my control.

I watched on as it broke free. As it leapt up onto our shared desk. As it pounded its breast like a valiant ape. And as it puffed its chest like a swashbuckling superhero.

The faint sound of Beethoven's Ninth Symphony started to fill my ears. Delicate violin strings provided a melodic backdrop for the ballet which was unravelling onstage.

My body performed a pirouette.

White paper rose up beneath my feet and span around my shins like froth on a choppy ocean.

I felt an all-encompassing surge of bliss.

One leg rose up in front of my body, forming a sharp arrow which pointed out towards an adjacent desk. I held that position perfectly still, whilst lifting my chin with a pompous sort of grace. Then I leapt like a spring deer, in slow motion, with one leg pointing forward and the other one darting back.

Beethoven's Ninth sounded glorious as it purred through the gears. Violas joined violins and cellos joined those violas. Double basses began to hum and flutes began to whistle.

I landed with my feet together; an angel of the air, a demon of the sea.

My mind floated atop an infinite ocean.

My legs leapt on through the infinite air. They bounded from table to table with ever-increasing speed; gaining momentum, gaining height. I could see my monkey soul. I could hear the monkey calls which were emanating from my open mouth.

I could hear Beethoven's Ninth reach its first crescendo, as the brass section began its battle cry. Flutes became one with clarinets. Bassoons boomed. Trumpets and horns squealed with uncontrollable delight.

I howled like a donkey at the moment of sexual climax.

My lungs filled with pure spirit.

I landed on all fours, looking like a bison. My shoulders were bulging out of my back and my temples were as erect as horns.

I leapt like a giant frog. And I stampeded between desks like a herd of untamed wildebeests; leaving a trail of overturned chairs, twisted students and miscellaneous debris in my wake.

Beethoven's Ninth called out for redemption, glory and release. It was an impassioned cry. It was a fury-filled yell.

"Yew! Yew! Yew!" Ms Brown yelled. "Yew! Yew! Yew!"

Ms Brown had been yelling since the moment I stood up. But I'd been on a different plane. I hadn't heard a thing.

My teacher's voice pierced my ether, burst my euphoria, and threw me down amongst the shards of my shattered pride. To my left; a small calculator bled black ink, a wonky table rocked back and forth like a sober addict, and a potted plant spewed crumbs of soil all across the vinyl flooring. To my right; Aisha Ali was crying into her collar, Tina Thompson was rubbing her shin, and Chubby Smith was holding his belly.

"Yew! Yew! Yew!" Ms Brown yelled.

(I'm called Yew by the way. I think I forgot to mention that).

"Yew! What on earth do you think you're doing? What's come over you? I, I, I..."

Ms Brown choked on her words, lifted a hand to her throat, coughed up some chalk-dust, and then gulped down a stodgy chunk of passive air.

She shook her head.

"You're usually such a good boy!"

She exhaled.

"I've never seen anything like it. Whatever came over you? Look at this place! Just look at this place! I... I... I just can't believe it! Oh my."

I looked around.

The debris of my liberation assaulted my torrid eyes. The disgrace of my emancipation flushed through my dusty veins. And my glorious body became a tepid vase for the desert's tears.

"I'm not angry," Ms Brown sighed. "I'm just disappointed."

That hurt. It hurt a lot.

I was fond of Ms Brown. She was such a sweet person. She was warm. So her disappointment really cut through me.

It was a heavy sort of disappointment; weighed down by the burden of expectation and the gravity of my situation. And it was an overpowering sort of disappointment. It pinned me to the floor.

My world inverted. Ignorance replaced enlightenment. Darkness replaced light. Density replaced levity.

My euphoria was usurped by a deathly sort of anxiety, which shook me from side to side and made me shiver to the core. Beethoven's Ninth was snuffed out by the booming of my incessant heart. I was sucked down into a black-hole at the centre of my being; paralysed by my teacher's disappointment and frozen by my own sense of fear. I felt trapped, small and base.

"Disappointed," Ms Brown repeated. "Yew! That's not how you're supposed to behave. That's not what society expects of you."

Ms Brown shook her head, which caused chalk-dust to float up into the air. It glistened in the bright-white light. It sparkled.

Ms Brown tutted.

Then she sent me to see the headmaster.

TWO

I never liked the headmaster's office. It just seemed to possess such a violent sort of neutrality. I was sure its eggshell walls and unassuming chairs were trying to assault me with their blandness.

For me, dear reader, that place was purgatory incarnate; neither good nor bad, but a gateway to great rewards or even greater punishments.

Like any sort of purgatory, real or imagined, it was the waiting that got to you. I had to sit there for over an hour; twiddling my thumbs and thumbing through a glossy edition of the Gideons International Bible. Mr Grunt, our headmaster, could have seen me straight away, but he chose not to.

"Come on Yew," he finally cheered. "We can't have you sitting there all day. Speak boy! Tell me why you're here. Can't you see I'm busy?"

Mr Grunt stared into my eyes.

The egot rolled its eyes.

I rocketed upright. My teeth chattered so much that I had to force my jaw open before I could speak:

"Ms Brown sent me, sir," I said in a whispered hush.

"Well, yes, of course she did. And why, may I ask, did Ms Brown send you here?"

"Because I behaved like a savage, sir. I leapt between tables like a monkey. And I stampeded around like an untamed wildebeest."

"Yew! Yewy Shodkin!" Mr Grunt gasped. He sounded more surprised than angry. "Why on earth would you do such a thing? Oh my! That's not how we behave. What came over you? You're usually such a good boy."

I looked down at my toes.

"The creature who lives inside my brain suggested I do it," I offered tentatively. "It was very convincing."

The egot nodded sagely and thumbed its chin. It looked like it was studying the situation; gathering evidence for use at a later point. But it didn't say a word.

Mr Grunt looked baffled. He squinted so much that his scraggly eyebrows merged. They looked like a wiry bush.

Mr Grunt didn't seem to know what to say. He just tapped his finger on his desk. Then he looked out through a nondescript plastic window.

"You think that a little creature lives in your brain?" he finally asked. "And that creature tells you what to do?"

"No sir," I replied. "It doesn't usually tell me what to do. It's never even spoken before."

"But you do believe that there's a creature living inside your brain?"

"Yeah, of course. It's always lived there."

"And that creature told you to run around like a savage?"

"Well, it didn't so much 'tell' me sir. It sort of suggested the idea. It sort of convinced me that it was what *I* really wanted to do."

Mr Grunt's eyes became translucent orbs of mixed-emotions. Full of intrigue, confusion and horror; consideration, deliberation and distress.

He looked down at his desk to avert my gaze. And then he wrote something inelegible on a plain pad of recycled paper.

The left half of his body jittered.

A hair fell from his nose.

"Yes, well, err," he said.

I nodded.

The egot nodded.

A bug nodded.

"Well, I think we need to get you some help then, dear boy. Don't you worry about a thing. We'll take good care of you! We're on *your* side!"

THREE

My mum kissed me on the cheek when she dropped me off at school. She always kissed me on the cheek when she dropped me off at school. She always hugged me. And she always said:

"Be a good boy, my angel. Don't do anything I wouldn't do!"

I looked at her. At the shoulder pads which propped up her cardigan, the liver spots which had laid siege to her hands, and those eyes of hers which were just so damn sincere. So honest. So utterly loving.

I smiled. And I made my way to the nurse's room, where I waited in a state of apprehensive silence.

The smell of antiseptic burned my nostrils and made my head tingle. That was the thing with the nurse's room; you went there to get better, but it often made you feel worse. It was sterile. It sparkled too much. It was just a little too clean for comfort.

Dr Saeed entered, sat down on a bony armchair, and then began:

"We're going to play a game," she said. "It's called 'Word Association'. I'll say one word, and I'd like you to reply with the first word that pops into your head.

"Do you understand?"

I nodded.

"Okay, let's give this a go…"

Dr Saeed didn't seem like a real doctor. She didn't have that muffled mix of power and compassion that hangs like a fug around most medics. And she didn't wear a stethoscope or a cape. She didn't even perform any examinations. She just talked and played games. But that was fine with me. Playing those games got me out of my maths class!

"Ice-" she said with the earnest look of a discerning professor.

"Cream," I replied.

"Monsters-"

"Scary"

"Real-"

"Me"

"Make believe-"

"Cartoons"

"Lion-"

"Roar!!!"

"Savage-"

"Free"

"Apple-"

"Orange"

"Fact-"

"Lessons"

"Fiction-"

"Cartoons"

"Little creatures-"

"Cartoons!"

As we played, Dr Saeed filled out a form; ticking off boxes and scribbling down notes in a particularly haphazard fashion.

She paused. Then she looked up at me for the briefest of moments. Her face looked utterly sincere. Serious. Blank.

Then it softened. Dr Saeed looked as if she was about to smile. But she resisted the urge and maintained her nonpartisan expression.

"Okay," she said. "I'm going to show you some pictures. I want you to tell me what you see."

I nodded.

The egot frowned. Its red forehead turned puce and magnolia. It looked like it was in a state of deep contemplation; judging Dr Saeed. But it didn't say a word. It just paced up and down the alleys of my brain's motor strip; nodding its head and twisting its whiskers.

Dr Saeed placed a pile of A4 cards on her lap and then flipped the first one up against her bosom. It featured a picture of a cat and a dog who were both chasing after the same ball.

I looked back at Dr Saeed.

"What do you see?" she nudged.

"A picture," I replied.

"Yes. Go on…"

"I see a picture."

"What's in the picture?"

"A cat and a dog."

"And what are they doing?"

"They're chasing a ball."

"How does that make you feel?"

"Huh?"

"What emotions do you feel when you look at this picture?"

"I don't feel anything."

"Nothing at all?"

"No. It's stupid. Cats don't chase after balls."

Dr Saeed nodded. She flipped through her cards, which all featured random scenes. And she continued to ask her random questions.

Then she came to a picture of a young boy. A little angel was standing on one of his shoulders and a little demon was standing on the other.

I looked back at Dr Saeed.

"What do you see?" she nudged.

"A boy with an angel and a demon on his shoulders."

"And what does that mean?"

"Mean?"

"What's the message?"

"It's a picture."

"But what's the picture trying to say?"

I giggled. It was one of this unwelcome giggles which spurt out of you sometimes. It was a girly giggle; both ear-splittingly shrill and tepidly twee. It was embarrassing. So I swallowed it down as quickly as I could. And then I answered the doctor in a haughty voice:

"Pictures don't speak," I said. "Pictures don't say anything at all."

The egot smiled.

Dr Saeed scowled.

"Why do you think there's an angel on the boy's shoulder?" she asked.

"Perhaps it got lost," I replied.

"Lost?"

"Yeah, lost. Angels belong in heaven. And that's not heaven - there's a demon there. You don't get demons in heaven."

The nauseous aroma of bleach skipped through the disinfected air.

"Do you think the angel might be there to speak to the boy?"

"Eh?"

"The angel and the demon are both stood with the boy. Usually, when people stand together, they end up talking. Do you think the characters in this picture might end up talking?"

"I dunno."

"You don't know?"

"Well, maybe. I can't see it, but I suppose it's possible."

Dr Saeed flipped her cards back down onto her lap.

"Do angels and demons ever speak to you?" she asked.

She tilted her head and gazed into my eyes.

"No," I replied. "I've never seen an angel or a demon before. Not in real life."

Dr Saeed took a deep breath.

"Yew," she said. "Last week you told Mr Grunt that a demon told you to destroy your classroom. Is that correct?"

"No," I replied. "I didn't say that. That's not what happened."

I meant what I was saying. To me, the egot wasn't a '*demon*'. It was a friend. And it didn't '*tell*' me to destroy the classroom. It suggested that I act like a savage. There's a difference. A big, big difference.

"Yew?"

"Yes."

"Are you telling the truth?"

"Yes Miss."

"So you didn't tell your headmaster that you heard a voice inside your head?"

"Well, yeah, I did tell him that."

"And that voice belonged to a demon?"

"No. Not a demon."

"Where did that voice come from?"

"From a creature."

"What sort of creature?"

"A strange one. But a nice one."

"And this creature, it spoke to you?"

"Yes."

"And it lives inside your head?"

Dr Saeed's questions were unsettling me. I felt that I was being interrogated, like a defendant in a court of law. I was in the dock and Dr Saeed was my prosecutor. The hangman's noose was waiting. Loose lips could swing the verdict.

I didn't say a word.

Dr Saeed didn't move an inch.

The egot skipped through the corridors of my mind, slid down a tendon, and ran a spindly claw through its bright yellow hair. It finally looked like it was ready to speak.

"Well, hello!" it said in its quiet voice; taking a full five seconds to say the word 'well', and echoing the word 'hello'. "If you want to get out of here you should probably deny my existence. Maybe tell the good doctor that you invented me. I expect they'll think you're mad if you tell them the truth. And they do horrible things to mad people. Horrible, horrible things. No, I don't think you'd want that. No, no."

I was supposed to tell the truth. That's what good boys do.

"Horrible, horrible things," the egot repeated.

It bounced its belly as if it was a ball.

"They put mad people in straightjackets, in padded cells. They feed them gruel. Sticky, grey gruel. Nothing else, only gruel. And they electrocute them every day.

"Horrible, horrible things. No, you wouldn't want that."

The egot sank back into my brain matter, like a cat in a beanbag, and removed a piece of chicken from its claw.

"I'm only telling you what you want to hear," it said without looking up. "You can get away with this. You can avoid those horrible things."

Dr Saeed cleared her throat.

"And it lives inside your head?" she repeated.

I looked down at my feet.

"No Miss," I replied.

"Where does the creature live?"

"There's no creature, Miss."

I paused for effect.

"I made it up Miss. I'm sorry."

My body didn't know how to react. My heart pounded against my innards; '*Boom! Smash! Boom, boom, smash!*' My stomach vibrated. My chest shook.

I felt queasy. I felt sick.

"Really Yew?"

"Yes Miss, really. I didn't want to take responsibility for my actions. It was ever so naughty of me. I really do feel ashamed."

Dr Saeed sat there in silence; staring at me with those earnest eyes of hers and that impartial face.

I was silent too.

It's like Lao Tzu says; '*Silence is a source of great strength*'.

Well, I wanted to show '*great strength*'.

And, in the end, it worked. Dr Saeed broke the silence before I did:

"Have you ever heard voices?" she asked me after many minutes had passed. "Have you ever heard voices inside your head?"

"Never," I lied. "Not even once."

FOUR

I was made to see to Dr Saeed every week.

She probed gently; interrogating me like a loquacious detective. But I don't think I ever said much myself. I spent most of my time playing with the doctor's wooden train set. I was fascinated by that thing. I loved its spinning wheels and its clunky track.

Dr Saeed wrote lots of notes. And I mean <u>lots</u> of notes. Reams of the things! In lined notebooks and on blank pads. Using gaudy ink and ashen pencil. Her endless squiggles usurped countless pages. Her meandering pen created a never-ending maze of tangled lines.

Then, after a year had passed, Dr Saeed packed those notes away, skedaddled and never returned. I had to attend maths classes after that.

I wasn't entirely sure why Dr Saeed upped and left. But I think the egot might have had a part to play. It was my guide. It helped me to steer clear of the traps which were hidden in Dr Saeed's innocuous questions.

The egot had begun to visit me on a regular basis. Its sage advice had protected me from precarious situations. And its mischievous temperament had lifted a curtain on my self-restraint. I'd started to do the things I'd always wanted to do, deep down, but had never had the courage to perform.

Please understand, dear reader, that I'm only talking about small things. And it has been said that small things amuse small minds. Perhaps I *did* have a small mind. But Lao Tzu says to '*Achieve greatness in little things*'. And I guess that was what I was trying to do.

One morning, for example, our class was waiting to go to assembly. Our teacher that year, Mr O'Donnell, had left the room. So I took advantage. Yes I did! I got all the girls in our class to stand with their legs apart. And then I slid on my back beneath them.

Gavin Gillis joined me. You could always rely on Gavin to join in the fun. He was such a good egg, that lad. He had a sense of mischief which was almost equal to my own. And he always had the best packed-lunches, which he shared with all his friends. Yeah, I really liked Gavin.

Anyway, Gavin and I slid between the girls' legs. We saw all their knickers! We saw them all!

Amy McLeish's were pink with white polka-dots. Kelly Evans's were like something out of the eighteen-hundreds; giant things the colour of a brown paper bag. And Chantelle Stevens wore a slinky thong. She was only seven years old, the devious little minx!

It was a violation; a violation of those girls and a violation of society's expectations. One simply wasn't supposed to do that sort of thing. But it felt great. It felt like I'd satisfied a gnawing urge. Like Gavin and I had released our inner-beasts; our true, savage selves.

The egot had encouraged me to do it.

"You'd like to see their knickers," it had prompted whist leaning against my brainstem. "This might be your only chance. You'll get away with it. And you'll like it. Think of all those beautiful little panties."

The egot spoke so quietly that I couldn't help but give it my undivided attention. It spoke with such indifference, as if unconcerned with my presence, that it pulled me in. The sweet melody in its voice put me into a heady trance. It intoxicated me. It threw me down onto the ground and propelled me beneath those untouched thighs and virgin groins; sucking in their femininity; frolicking in my wayward tomfoolery.

But it'd be wrong to blame the egot for my behaviour. The truth is that I'd wanted to look up those girls' skirts. I'd had an insatiable urge to get close to that forbidden fruit. The egot had helped me to overcome my inhibitions, but it hadn't turned me into another person. Far from it.

Lao Tzu says, '*When you are content to be yourself, without comparing or competing, everybody will respect you*'.

Well, I was being '*myself*'. My real self. And I think my classmates did '*respect*' me for that. No-one told Mr O'Donnell what we'd done. Gavin and I got away with our indiscretions, just as the egot had predicted.

I got away with a lot over the months which followed.

I got away with copying Snotty McGill's classwork. I got away with eating a chocolate bar I took from Mr McDonnell's desk. And I got away with urinating in a plant pot. Twice! Although I did get caught the third time I did it.

"Put on an innocent face," the egot told me. Its own face faded from a guilty shade of red to a coy shade of pink. "Tell Mr McDonnell you're sorry. You couldn't hold it in. You'll never do it again.

"I'm sure he'll be sympathetic. Yes, yes."

Mr McDonnell listened as I repeated the egot's words. He rolled his eyes and then continued on with the class.

Coltish smiles flickered across my classmates' cheeky faces. Their stifled giggles rang in my ears. I was sure they were laughing with me, not at me. And that made me feel so proud! So rebellious! So darn-tooting invincible!

I puffed my chest. I felt like I was the king of my castle and the master of my class.

I was caught again the fifth time I peed in the plant pot. As a punishment, I was made to use a potty for two weeks. That was pretty embarrassing. It brought me down to earth with a real bump.

The plant died.

I stopped urinating in public.

And I started to receive other little punishments too.

I had to sit cross-legged on the floor, facing a sudatory radiator, the time I used Sleepy Sampson's sleeve as a handkerchief. My face became as red as a prostitute's lamp and my legs became completely numb. But I was back at my desk within thirty minutes.

I was made to sit in silence when I pulled a moony. But I still whispered to my friends, to stand up for myself, and to rail against the system. The egot told me to do it. It puffed its chest and I puffed mine.

And I was made to read a book whilst my classmates were outside learning about plants, because I'd farted really loudly during a school assembly. It was a particularly squishy fart, if the truth be told. That was a little naughty. It made the egot laugh.

But none of those punishments ever stopped me from listening to the egot.

The egot encouraged me to hide the chalk, in a failed attempt to stop our maths class from going ahead. It encouraged me to reset the clocks, so that we'd be able to leave school an hour early. That almost worked. And it encouraged me to cut clumps out of Stacey Fairclough's hair. Well, I felt I was doing her a favour; she looked so sweet whenever she had short hair.

I got away with all those things and more. It made me feel pretty damn invincible. It made me feel pretty damn great indeed!

FIVE

Each time I listened to the egot I felt a little freer. A little happier.

The egot was my drug. When I followed its suggestions, I got high. For sure, getting caught was like a comedown; wretched, sickly and bleak. But I became ambivalent to my shame, I overcame my guilt, and I survived my punishments. I still wanted more. I still *craved* more.

I was addicted.

But that all changed when I overdosed on the egot's advice...

It happened on a crisp spring morning; on one of those dewy days where the ground is luminous and the air is forever fresh. But I was stuck inside, and the stifling nature of school was getting to me. I'm a bird, you see; I need to fly free. I need space and freedom. And, back then, I needed to be a child; to frolic like a child, laugh like a child, and cause mischief like a child. But there I was, forced to sit behind a desk; held captive by four insensitive walls and enslaved by my teacher's omnipotent authority.

I suppose, being stuck inside like that caused me to contract what Richard Louv calls 'Nature Deficit Disorder'. It's a disorder that develops when a person doesn't spend enough time outdoors. As well as leading to a wide range of behavioural problems, Nature Deficit Disorder can also dull the senses, increase the rate of illness, and lead to attention difficulties. According to Dr Stephanie Wear, being stuck inside can increase your stress hormones, blood pressure and resting heartbeat.

But, if you'd asked me about how I felt back then, I wouldn't have intellectualized things in that manner. I wouldn't have mentioned the likes of Louv or Wear. That's not how my mind worked.

My issues were emotional. I *felt* them. I felt trapped by the drip-drip indoctrination of the national curriculum. I felt like a prisoner in that stuffy classroom. And I felt that I was losing my individuality; wearing a generic school uniform and following a generic set of school rules.

I just didn't feel natural. I didn't feel right. I wanted to break free, run around, and revel in the playground of infinity. I wanted to be young. I wanted to be a member of that endangered species; the child in its natural environment.

I inhaled, sighed, and gazed out of the window.

I saw a rainbow. To me, it looked like a crown atop the sky. It was beautiful. Vibrant. Dazzling.

The violet was so vivid! The indigo was so indulgent! The red was so real!

My glutinous eyes feasted on that rainbow. It filled me with wonder. I could feel its magic. I was entranced by its mystery.

I wanted to run out of our classroom and chase that rainbow down. I wanted to dig up the pots of gold which were buried at either end. I wanted to twirl in that rainbow's colourful vapour and frolic in its luminous mist.

I wanted to take my shoes off and feel the grass between my toes.

I wanted to dance in the rain.

But I couldn't. I had to stay inside, trapped within that airless classroom. Suffocating. Feeling restless, tense and twitchy.

And so, during Mr O'Donnell's seventh lesson on past participles, I started to laugh out loud. I laughed for the sake of laughing. Belly-laugh followed belly-laugh. Thunderous guffaws knocked me over. And hearty convulsions forced me to roll around.

I was following the egot's advice:

"Let go," it whispered to me whilst tipping its flat cap. The word 'go' had echoed four times; '*Go-go-go-go*'.

"Break free. Be free. Be the boy you want to be. Yes, yes!"

So I started to laugh. Just like that. I did exactly as the egot had suggested. And it felt so right! So good! So natural!

The egot started to howl.

Then I started to howl. I howled for the sake of howling. I howled like a rapturous wolf. I released a never-ending '*Ah-woo*', which floated on the wings of time and soared as high as the heavens. I released my inner-beast. It was base. It was animalistic. And it felt great.

'*Ah-woo! Ah-woo! Ah-woo!*'

I must've howled for a full three minutes.

Mr O'Donnell marched across the classroom, taking slow methodical steps. He stopped still. And then he stood above me, with his hands on his pointy hips.

His shadow engulfed me. His breath burnt my neck.

He waited, as still as a sentry, until I'd finished. And then he returned to the front of the room, where he continued on with the lesson as if nothing had happened. But I could tell that he'd been affected. His hands shook as he wrote. And his voice stuttered as he spoke:

"What is the su-su-subjunctive form of a vu-vu-verb?" he asked.

"Shouldn't you know that?" I replied at the egot's request. "You're supposed to be the teacher."

Mr O'Donnell snapped his piece of chalk.

Sleepy Sampson giggled like a toddler.

And an announcement blared out of the PA:

"Daisy Smith: Please report to reception immediately."

Mr O'Donnell paused. He stood there, with his hands on his hips, whilst he waited for the interruption to finish.

The PA fizzled.

Mr O'Donnell was about to continue, but I spoke up before he had the chance:

"I'm hearing those voices again," I said.

Everyone laughed.

Mr McDonnell cracked.

"Yew!" he yelled. "Yew Shodkin! I've had it up to here with you. This is your last warning! You're walking a thin line now boy-o. If I hear another peep out of you today, you'll find yourself in front of Mr Grunt. Serious disciplinary measures will await! Oh yes!"

But I didn't care. I was still on edge; full of restless energy and unfulfilled cravings. I still felt imprisoned. I still felt an urge to break free.

So, at the egot's suggestion, I picked up a wooden ruler and slapped it against Chubby Smith's arm.

"Yee-ha!!!" the egot whooped. Its voice was still quiet, even though it was cheering, which imbued it with a sort of understated gravitas.

Chubby Smith's eyes lit up.

I jabbed his breast. I stabbed his arm. I swished the breath from his mouth.

Chubby Smith grabbed his ruler.

"Touché!" he cheered as he thrust it towards me.

God I loved that boy! Chubby Smith was a real legend. He had that air of joviality which you often find in the slightly rotund. A smile was never far from his lips. His eyes were always inclined to a cheeky wink.

I swatted his ruler aside and leapt to my feet.

"En garde!"

Chubby Smith jumped up. He was beaming!

We faced off.

I lunged forward, with my head bowed and my ruler outstretched. Chubby Smith bent backwards. His stumpy legs stumbled through a thousand tiny steps.

He recovered. He gave me a cheeky wink. And then he went on the offensive; swinging and jabbing; slashing his ruler through the nonchalant air. I dodged and ducked and dived; bobbing one way and then the other.

The egot mimicked my movements. There was a joyous smile on its face. Its hair glowed. Its red skin glistened with fiery sweat.

We skipped around the room.

We always used to skip back then. It was an expression of our youth; more joyous than walking, more graceful than running, and more weightless than standing still.

We skipped past busy shelves, sickly plants and baffled students.

We skipped past the school mouse, who was imprisoned in a tiny cage.

We skipped past tables, chairs and cupboards.

And we danced. Screeching chairs slid away as we waltzed between them. Girls gasped as we exchanged blows. Boys cheered as my ruler prodded Chubby Smith's ribs, triceps and hips. As he responded with blows to my abdomen, wrist and kidney.

The repressive walls melted away. Letters, numbers and words floated off into the ether. Rules, regulations and restrictions fell to the ground like dust.

I was breaking free from the shackles of my incarceration. I was expressing myself. And, above all else, I was being a child; playing games, burning off my excess energy, and having the time of my life.

The egot was having the time of its life.

Mr O'Donnell was yelling:

"Yew Shodkin! This time you've done it! Oh yes!"

He was scrambling across the room; lumbering over chairs and crashing into children. His brown brogues were slapping the waxy linoleum. His sleeves were flapping about like demented bird-wings.

"You're in trouble now boy-o!"

Mr O'Donnell swept down on me, grabbed my collar and lifted me up like an eagle with a mouse. My top button cut into my throat. My legs caught the air.

It was the start of my comedown.

My world inverted. The sparks of freedom which had burned inside me were snuffed out by Mr O'Donnell's foggy breath. My hope was replaced by fear.

Mr O'Donnell carried me outside.

On we marched; through plastic-coated halls which smelt of white glue, around barbed corners and up lonesome steps. My teacher's feet tapped a manic beat; out of time and without any rhythm.

The walls gawked at me with condescending aloofness.

The air tasted of years gone by.

My heart pounded. It echoed with foreboding. My neck-hairs stood to attention. My feet cried sweaty tears.

On we marched; through the luminous glare of neon tube-lighting, around vainglorious cupboards and up toothy stairs.

On we marched; through the alleys of my discontent, the passageways of my perdition and the labyrinths of my shame.

On we marched, until we reached Mr Grunt's office, where we stood to attention and awaited orders.

"And what do we have here then?" The headmaster boomed.

"This boy-o has gone too far," Mr O'Donnell replied. "Too far! He's been tearing around, fighting, talking back and howling. It's time for some serious disciplinary action. Oh yes!"

Mr Grunt's head bobbed up and down.

"Serious disciplinary actions?" he echoed.

"Some serious discipline," Mr O'Donnell agreed. "Oh yes!"

Mr Grunt took a moment to think. His bushy eyebrows pressed together. His elephantine skin crumpled into folds.

The seconds which followed felt like little pieces of eternity. Everything was quiet. Even the echoes were silent. Even the wind shushed itself.

My teachers loomed over me; suffocating me with their negative energy and sucking every ounce of élan from my shattered being. I could feel their auras. I could see the brown of their self-absorption, the dark yellow of their stress, and the muddy red of their anger.

That anger bubbled away. Smoke poured out of their busy nostrils. And lava flowed through their bloodshot eyes.

I felt so small! I felt like a mouse who'd been trapped in a corner by a patient cat. My fear strangled me. My guilt rattled me. My shame erupted. I felt disgraced, ridiculous and utterly absurd.

"Have you ever heard the expression," Mr Grunt finally asked. "'*Fool me once, shame on you. Fool me twice, shame on me*'?"

I shook my head. The motion made my stomach feel queasy.

Mr Grunt tapped his finger.

"You've been making '*fools*' out of us," he sighed. "We've given you chance-after-chance and you've '*shamed*' us time-after-time. We need to do things differently. We need to discipline you."

Mr Grunt looked at Mr O'Donnell for approval.

Mr O'Donnell nodded sagely.

My belly filled with acid.

"Yes," Mr Grunt continued. "Discipline! Serious disciplinary measures!"

He tapped his weather-beaten lip.

"We don't like to discipline our students. No. We don't enjoy it one bit. But we *do* need to do it. We need to do it for our students' sake - to help them to become better people. It's our duty."

Mr Grunt looked pleased with himself.

"Do you know why people prune their plants?" he asked.

I shrugged.

"To eat them?" I asked tentatively.

Mr Grunt laughed. It was a warm laugh. Uncle-like. Gay.

"No Yewy, it's not to eat them. It's because when you cut back the plants' dominant stems, you give its weaker stems the chance to grow. In time, the plant will flourish. It'll produce prettier flowers and bigger fruit."

I nodded.

But I couldn't be sure what Mr Grunt was getting at. And so I started to doubt my rational capabilities. I started to doubt my sanity. I started to doubt everything:

'What was I doing?'

'Why on earth did I howl like a wolf?'

'Why did I have a sword fight with Chubby Smith?'

'Why did I have to be so different?'

'Why couldn't I just conform, like all the other kids in my class?'

My doubt mixed in with my shame. It created a maelstrom of acid in my stomach and a cyclone of blood in my heart.

Mr Grunt, on the other hand, was grinning like a Cheshire cat. The blood which had drained from my face seemed to have re-appeared in his. His eyebrows had finally split into two distinct entities.

He continued on:

"Well, young Yew, your personality is dominated by a few malignant stems. Stems of mischief! Stems of indiscipline! Stems of moral depravity!

"But *there are* stems of decency in you as well. Stems of intelligence. Stems of fraternity. Stems of confidence.

"We need to discipline you."

Mr Grunt paused for the briefest of moments, which allowed Mr O'Donnell to echo his words:

"We need to discipline you boy-o! Oh yes!"

Mr Grunt cleared his throat:

'Aargh! Gumph!'

"Well, yes, exactly," he continued. "We need to discipline you. But we don't *want* to discipline you. No. We're not nasty. We're not bad people.

"Think of us as gardeners. We want to help you to develop and grow! But, before you can bloom, we need to prune back the nasty character traits which are dominating your personality. It'll allow your good side to blossom. It'll help you to become a better you!"

The headmaster's words seemed so elegant to me. So refined. So utterly cerebral!

But, looking back on it now, I can't help thinking of a Lao Tzu proverb; *'True words are not beautiful, beautiful words are not true. Good words are not persuasive, persuasive words are not good'*.

I found Mr Grunt's words *'beautiful'* and *'persuasive'*. I found them intoxicating. But, overwhelmed by the presence of those two grown men,

I couldn't see that Mr Grunt's words were neither '*good*' nor '*true*'.

My eyes opened wide.

And then it hit me. It had taken me what felt like millennia, but it finally hit me. I finally realised why I was feeling so depraved.

It was that little blighter, the egot!

The egot had always protected me when I'd gotten into trouble. It had always helped me to overcome the punishments and harsh-words which came my way. It had always made me feel invincible.

But, in the tumultuous furore which had enveloped me, I hadn't even noticed its absence. I hadn't even thought of it.

Mr O'Donnell stood above me. Mr Grunt sat in front of me. And I looked inside myself to find the egot.

I soon located it. It was sat, with its back turned, scratching its elfish ears. It looked like it was talking to itself; opening and closing its mouth without emitting a sound. It looked utterly confused. Broken. Lost.

I tried to get its attention, but it didn't even look up.

I shook my head. I shouted at the egot. I stared at it. But it didn't move an inch. It completely ignored me!

It counted and re-counted its claws.

A silver tear rolled down its cheek.

A hair fell from its head.

I was gobsmacked. Flabbergasted. I felt totally betrayed.

I hit rock bottom for the first time since I was admonished for acting like a savage. Like that time, I felt a deathly sort of anxiety, which shook me from side to side and made me shiver to the core. I felt abandoned, small and base.

I simply couldn't comprehend what had happened. I couldn't process the information which was revealing itself to me. I couldn't cope with the egot's betrayal.

The egot was just sitting there, rocking. Oblivious to me. Oblivious to my needs.

It had totally abandoned me at the moment I'd needed it the most.

My fingertips tingled and my insides felt totally hollow.

"We need to discipline you, Yewy," Mr Grunt concluded.

"You need discipline boy-o," Mr O'Donnell replied.

"Well, err, yes," Mr Grunt continued. "Report to me after lunch to start your punishment."

I bowed my head.

I couldn't muster the strength to reply.

SIX

I changed.

If you were to ask Mr O'Donnell or Mr Grunt, they'd probably tell you that their disciplinary measures made the difference. But they'd be wrong.

It's like Lao Tzu says; *'If you are untrustworthy, people will not trust you'*.

Well, for me, the egot had become *'untrustworthy'*. I couldn't *'trust'* it. I didn't feel that I could rely on its advice.

So I ignored the egot when it told me to rebel; to go and play with the other kids rather than return to see the headmaster. I went to see Mr Grunt as soon as I'd eaten my lunch.

Mr Grunt sat me down in the school's reception. Then he told me to write this line fifty times:

'My good side will overpower my bad side. My angels will overcome my demons. My light will outshine my darkness'.

The egot swung between cranial nerves, like a beastly Tarzan who had free rein over the jungle of my mind. It let go, flew through some empty space, and landed with an *'Oomph'*. Its red skin glistened with sweat and its yellow hair hung with a scruffy sort of animal magnetism.

It smiled at me. It was such an innocent smile. Beguiling. Mesmeric.

The egot lifted its flat cap, bent its knee, and winked in a way which made its eye sparkle. It made me feel warm and fuzzy inside.

The egot was just *so* seductive. It still held sway over my emotions.

"You don't really want to write lines," it said in its *oh-so-quiet* voice; mulling over the letter 'd' in the word 'don't' like a melancholic opera singer. "I think you'd like to refuse Mr Grunt's request. You wouldn't want to look weak. No, no."

I didn't say a word.

"If you succumb now, you'd be made to endure months of punishments. Chances are you'd be better off if you stood up for yourself."

The egot's melodic voice rocked me into a heady trance. Its toxic charm hypnotized me. I was on the verge of taking its advice.

"Uh. The thing is. I, err. I, umm," I stuttered.

But then I remembered the headmaster's words:

'*We don't want to discipline you. No. We want to help you to develop and grow!*'

Mr Grunt was gazing into my eyes. He had the look of a benign dictator. He looked like a cross between Santa Claus and King Arthur.

"This will help you to become a better you," he prompted.

I nodded. My head was bowed and my eyes were fixed on the floor.

I picked up my pen and began to write.

I did it for a selfish reason; to avoid further punishment. And I did it for a selfless reason too; to please Mr Grunt. Even though he was hurting me, I still wanted to make him happy. That selfless urge ran deep within me.

Anyway, as soon as Mr Grunt turned his back, the egot piped up again.

"You don't want to write those lines," it said. "Not if you're being honest with yourself."

I wrote another line.

The egot strummed its lip.

"If you *are* going to write lines," it continued. "You could always write *different* lines. Just to show a little of your character. To stand up for yourself in the smallest of ways. You could write; '*My stems will not be cut. My hands will not be tied*'. If you want to, that is. Yes, yes."

I ignored it. I ignored that little blighter, just like it had ignored me when I'd needed it the most.

Please understand, dear reader, that I'm not suggesting it was easy. Oh no! Deep down I knew the egot was right. I didn't want to write those lines. I wanted to run out of that place. I wanted to play, outside, with all my friends.

But my world had crumbled around me. The egot had got me into deep trouble. And then it had deserted me! I was having to write lines because of that charlatan! So I was in no mind to listen to it again.

Of course, there *were* still reasons to listen to the egot; the highs were there to be had. The euphoria I'd felt the first time I listened to the egot was a heaven-sent nirvana. It was emancipating. Enlightening. Bliss.

And I'd experienced that sort of high several times since. Just not quite as intensely. Listening to the egot hadn't ever made me feel as good as it had done that first time. The euphoria had never been quite as heady. The release had never been quite as profound.

At the same time, my comedowns were getting worse. I was getting punished more regularly than ever before. And those punishments were leaving me low.

Well, it was those lows, and not the highs, which were taking centre stage in the arena of my thoughts.

The scales had tipped.

A white flag was fluttering in the unenthusiastic breeze. A pen was in my hand. And a blank sheet of paper was filling up with the lines of my surrender.

SEVEN

The egot was right about one thing. My decision to write those lines did put Mr Grunt on the front foot. His confidence grew as quickly as mine diminished. His punishments came thick and fast...

I had to stay inside, writing lines, every day after I'd eaten my lunch. And, dear reader, some of those lines were quite frankly bizarre.

Here's a few examples:

'I will not interrupt the class unless I'm vomiting, bleeding or on fire'.

'Good boys don't eat their shoes, stuff mulch down their pants, or glue food to the table'.

'Students should not engage in lamprophony. They should be pauciloquent'.

Writing those lines wasn't so bad, per se, but I did resent losing my lunch break. I needed the fresh air. I needed to be social. But I was stuck, alone, in that soulless school reception; that stolid, empty space, where the air was always dank and the silence was always snooty.

The egot always encouraged me to act out.

One day, for example, it suggested that I release the school mouse:

"He wants to be free, just like you," it prompted whilst ruffling about in my parietal lobe. "Perhaps you should let him run around in the corridor. Let go. Float away. Do what you really want to do. Yes, yes."

Another time, whilst sweating away in that unventilated box of a room, the egot suggested that I run away and jump in a lake. And on a third occasion it suggested that I lick the wall. (Well, I did happen to be wondering what it'd taste like).

The egot suggested that I stand up for myself, act out and rebel, every single time I was given lines. And every time I ignored it.

I ignored it when Mr Grunt told me that I'd be spending my morning breaks picking up litter. Although, if I'm to tell the truth, I actually quite liked that 'punishment'. It got me outside and it gave me something to focus on.

I also ignored the egot when I was told to run around the football pitch instead of taking part in PE lessons. And I ignored it when I was made to miss a class field trip. I complied with every single punishment which came my way.

And those punishments didn't stop at school.

My parents, you see, were a little square. They cared more about being good parents in the general sense than being good parents for me. They wanted to appear normal; respectable and responsible. But they weren't prepared to acknowledge my individual needs.

And so, given my behaviour, they did what they felt society would want. They refused to stand up for me. They didn't protect me from my teachers' wrath. Not once! They colluded with my teachers! They supported the school on every single issue. Dear reader, they turned on me! They punished me themselves!

Whenever I got home my parents sent me to my room. I had to stay in there, on my own, for weeks on end. It was boring; I didn't have a TV or a radio. There was absolutely nothing to do.

I was only ever given boring food to eat. There was no ice-cream or chocolate for old Yew!

My dad smacked me whenever I disobeyed him. *'Bang! Bang! Bang!'* His eyes glowed red. My bottom hurt something chronic.

And my mum washed my mouth out with soap whenever I swore.

"You need to be a good boy," she'd say. "Don't do anything I wouldn't do!"

I think those punishments made my mum feel uncomfortable. Those sincere, loving eyes of hers look distressed whenever she punished me; as if she was experiencing some of my pain herself. But my dad seemed to actually enjoy himself. His chin used to jut forwards when he punished me. His eyebrows used to jump for joy.

My parents' abandonment began to grate. It opened up a desolate crater within me. I felt like a grain of sand, thrown in random directions by an omnipotent ocean. I felt like a feather in the dawn breeze. I felt so low that I was tempted to listen to the egot.

"Just leave your room," it often suggested. "What are your parents going to do? There's nothing they can do! They won't have any power over you if you have power over yourself. No, no."

But I never listened to the egot.

The egot's words felt polluted. Their pull was powerful, their content was true. But they were weighed down with images of my fall. Whenever the egot spoke, I recalled the punishments I'd suffered after following its advice. I saw myself writing lines, picking up litter or sitting in my room.

The push of those punishments overpowered the egot's pull.

And so I walked on through those dark days with my head bowed and my tail between my legs. I ground the gears. I did everything that was expected of me, whenever it was expected, even when I didn't want to. I said 'please' and 'thank-you'. I only spoke when I was spoken to.

But I got by. I survived. Because, as I denied myself, other people began to accept me. The more my actions betrayed me, the more other people warmed to me. In that all-singing, all-dancing, madhouse of a world, my conformity was a cause for real celebration. And that did cheer me up. I liked making other people happy. I wanted to make them happy!

That selfless urge drove me on.

I knew I was pleasing people, because they told me so. Like when Mr Grunt patted me on the back after I'd been writing lines for three months:

"I knew we'd make a respectable citizen out of you," he sang with self-gratifying glee. "Doesn't the world feel like a better place now?"

It really didn't, but I still appreciated Mr Grunt's positive energy. It made me feel proud. My body flushed with a comfortable sort of warmth and my toes all tingled.

I also appreciated my parents' kind words:

"We're so very proud of you," they told me after another three months had passed. They took me bowling. My mum rubbed my thigh and my dad nodded. (He wasn't one for physical contact).

I enjoyed that outing. And I enjoyed the other treats I received when I behaved; the ice-creams, mangoes and chocolates; football boots, computer games and movies.

When I went for a whole month without getting into trouble, my mum took me to a waterpark where there were whirlpools, slides and Jacuzzis!

"You're such a good boy," she said. "You deserve to have some fun."

When I got knocked about on the train, but didn't fight back, my gran bought me some chewing gum.

And when I got ten out of ten on a test, Mr O'Donnell gave me a gold star. A genuine gold star! Just like all the good boys and girls used to get!

That sort of special treatment did lift my mood. It encouraged me to behave. Not, please understand, because I wanted to behave. Oh no! But solely because I wanted the rewards. I liked those rewards. And I liked making people happy.

For me, it was a bit like having a job; I was doing things I didn't want to do, in order to receive a payoff that I did want to receive. I suppose you could say I was a labourer, working at the feet of society's desires.

I was finally starting to fit in...

EIGHT

I didn't know it at the time, but my parents and teachers were using a process which psychologists call 'Operant Conditioning'. I don't think they knew they were using that process. I don't think they even knew what Operant Conditioning was. But they were using it nonetheless.

Operant Conditioning is based on Edward Thorndike's concept, the 'Law of Effect', which states that actions which are followed by pleasant consequences are more likely to be repeated, whilst actions which are followed by unpleasant consequences are less likely to be repeated.

It sounds like common sense, right?

Well, Operant Conditioning takes place where someone uses that natural law to alter the behaviour of another being; by creating pleasant consequences (such as rewards) to encourage desired forms of behaviour, or by creating unpleasant consequences (such as punishments) to discourage undesired forms of behaviour.

One of the first psychologists to prove that Operant Conditioning could work was Burrhus Skinner. Skinner set up an experiment in which a hungry rat was placed inside a box. Whenever it pressed a lever it was rewarded with a treat, which was delivered through a plastic tube.

At first, Skinner's rats acted in a random manner. But, in time, they all pressed the lever by accident, for which they received a treat. They soon realised that they could receive more treats by pressing the lever more times. And so they pushed the lever over and over again.

Operant Conditioning had converted those rats into lever pushers.

This form of Operant Conditioning is called 'Positive Reinforcement'.

Skinner then adapted his experiment. This time, the rats were subjected to an electronic current which ran across the floor.

The rats soon learnt to press the lever in order to stop that current.

Then Skinner introduced a light, which turned on just before the current.

In time, the rats learnt to tap the lever as soon that light came on, to avoid receiving an electric shock. Even when the electronic shocks were turned off, the rats still pressed the lever whenever they saw the light.

This form of Operant Conditioning is called 'Negative Reinforcement'.

Well, this partnership of punishments and rewards, bribes and threats, can be used to affect human behaviour too. This was shown by the 'Little Albert Experiment'.

In that trial, two psychologists showed baby Albert some masks, a monkey, a rabbit and a rat. I don't know what it is with psychologists and rats. I think they've got some sort of fixation on the little buggers. But anyway, little Albert was fine with all the things he was shown; he didn't react to them at all.

Then the psychologists struck a hammer against a steel bar. Little Albert burst into tears. The noise had terrified him.

When Albert was eleven months old, the psychologists showed him the rat again. As they did this, they hit the steel bar.

Little Albert burst into tears, because he was terrified by the noise. And he burst into tears every time this process was repeated, once a week, for seven weeks.

In the end, Albert associated the scary sound with the rat. And so he became fearful of the rat itself. He cried and tried to crawl away whenever he was shown it, even when the steel bar wasn't struck. And he acted in a similar manner whenever he saw other things which reminded him of the rat; things like the family dog, a fur coat, some cotton wool and a fake Father Christmas beard.

Well, that's exactly what happened to me!

My parents and teachers punished me whenever I misbehaved, which encouraged me not to misbehave. It was a case of Negative Reinforcement. And my parents also rewarded me when I was good, which encouraged me to behave. It was a case of Positive Reinforcement.

"Be a good boy," my mum used to say. "Don't do anything I wouldn't do!"

And I listened to her. But it never made me happy. Deep down, I didn't want to be a '*good boy*'. I just wanted the rewards which came when I behaved. And I did still want to do the sort of things my mother '*wouldn't do*'. But I didn't do those things because I was scared of being punished. Yes, I conformed. But, just like Albert and the rats, I don't think I was ever truly happy.

I mean, think about it. Skinner got those rats to behave exactly as he wished; he converted them into good little lever pushers. But do you think those rats were happy? Really happy? Do you think they liked being electrocuted? I mean, who likes being electrocuted? Don't you think those rats would have preferred to be free to run around the sewers, doing ratty things like eating cheese and gnawing on cables?

And what about little Albert? Do you think he wanted to be terrified of anything which remotely resembled a rat? He was acting exactly as the psychologists had hoped, but I doubt he was truly happy.

Well, I was the same. I wasn't happy. How could I be? I was living in a state of constant terror.

Whenever I wanted to do something naughty, whenever the egot convinced me to misbehave, I immediately thought of the painful punishments I'd have to endure.

My actions were all dictated by fear...

When I wanted to take my clothes off and run around naked, because it was just so hot inside, I saw myself in my school's reception, writing lines which just went on-and-on forever. In the end, I did remove my jumper, but I kept the rest of my clothes on.

When I wanted to throw my dinner onto the floor, because it was the most disgusting thing I'd ever tasted, I imagined myself locked up in my bedroom, bored out of my mind. So I ate that mangy meal.

And when I wanted to hide Sleepy Sampson's PE kit, so I could see her do PE in her underwear, I couldn't help but see my dad smack me, over and over again. *'Bang! Bang! Bang!'* Just thinking about it made my bottom feel physically sore. And so, in the end, I left Sleepy Sampson's PE kit exactly where it was.

My actions were all dictated by fear, just as had happened with little Albert.

Because little Albert heard a scary sound whenever he saw the rat, he associated that scary sound with the rat. He became scared of the rat itself.

In the same way, because I was punished whenever I misbehaved, I associated misbehaving with punishments. And so I became scared of misbehaving. Deep down, I still wanted to misbehave. The egot still encouraged me to misbehave. But that didn't come into the equation.

My good behaviour made other people happy; I was becoming the person they wanted me to be. But I don't think it ever made me happy. I don't think anyone can be happy whilst they're being coerced to act in an unnatural manner.

Lao Tzu says; *'When I let go of what I am, I become what I might be'*.

Well, I was certainly *'letting go'*. I was becoming what I *'might be'*. But it was tearing me up inside. Because I didn't want to be what I *'might be'*. I wanted to be me.

NINE

It wasn't just the Positive and Negative Reinforcements, the punishments and rewards, which kept me on the straight and narrow back then. I had a very important responsibility which also helped to keep me in line. You see, dear reader, I was the class Cupboard Monitor. And I was incredibly proud to hold such a haughty position!

Well, they do say that having responsibilities is good for one's personal confidence.

The classroom cupboard was three metres wide and two shelves tall. It was made of fibreboard, which was protected by a thin layer of beige plastic. It had six doors, eighteen hinges and one hundred and twenty-three screws. Yes, I did count them all. Twice.

That cupboard was a real mess when I first took up office. Pens were mixed in with pencils, the paint pots were covered in dust, and the exercise books were all facing in different directions.

But I soon fixed that!

By the time I was done, everything was in order and everything was clean. Everything had its place. The felt-tip pens were arranged according to colour. The pencils were lined up from shortest to tallest. And I even stuck little labels onto the shelves, to mark where each item belonged.

I think I must have had 'Obsessive Compulsive Disorder'.

I was so proud of that cupboard. It gave my mind something to focus on. And my work was appreciated too:

"There's my little lieutenant!" our teacher, Miss Grey used to say. She used to ruffle my hair, to show that she was pleased with me. And she used to smile at me in a way which was one part proud and one part seductive.

She was such a sweet person, that Miss Grey. She had these little dimples which pulsated when she was happy. And she always wore summery dresses which really lit up the room. They were covered in colourful flowers, pretty butterflies and retro patterns.

Mr Grunt also passed comment on my work:

"You're the best cupboard monitor this school has ever had," he told me one time.

I blushed with pride. My skin tingled. My teeth felt fizzy.

For the first time in my life, I was doing something that was both enjoyable *and* appreciated. I was starting to assimilate.

I liked the responsibility. I'd always acted out when I felt lost, imprisoned or feeble. I'd wanted autonomy. I'd wanted to have power over my actions. And that role gave me a power of sorts. I got to maintain that cupboard *my way*, as I deemed fit. My position gave me that responsibility. It gave me a stake in society. And I found that exhilarating.

I wouldn't let anyone mess with that cupboard. I was protective, like a big brother. I was defensive. And I was proud. Oh so proud!

But it's like Lao Tzu says; *'Pride brings about one's downfall'*.

And so it turned out. My *'pride'* did indeed lead to my *'downfall'*…

It all started when Snotty McGill put the scissors back in the wrong place. Well, dear reader, the egot took its cue!

The egot, you see, had remained a permanent feature in the landscape of my mind. It was still very much at home in there; lounging on my beefy sinews and swinging between my brain's different lobes. But it didn't speak so much. It had lost some of its aura. It had become a *persona non grata*; subdued by my will to resist it.

The egot gazed up at me.

It'd be wrong to say it had puppy dog eyes. The egot was too suave for that. But there was an element of desperation in the way it looked at me. It didn't bend its knee in its normal fashion. Rather, it stood perfectly erect. And its voice sounded tepid. The egot had to use such much energy to open its mouth that it didn't have the strength to fully activate its vocal cords.

"Yew?" it whispered. "Yew?"

The egot put a finger in the air and waited for permission to speak.

I nodded.

"You didn't like that, did you?"

I nodded again.

"People shouldn't mess with your system, should they?"

I shook my head.

"Well then, it might be a good idea to pull Snotty McGill's hair. She should know that she's misbehaved. *You* get punished when you misbehave, so *she* should get punished too. It's only fair."

I pulled Snotty McGill's hair.

I did it without even thinking. And I regretted it straight away. I regretted it even as I was doing it!

"*Eeeeeeeeee*," Snotty McGill screamed.

It was an ear-splitting scream; as sharp as a razor and as shrill as a maternal monkey. It cut through me like a knife through butter.

The gravity of my situation weighed down on me.

It took me a moment to appreciate what I'd done. And then it all became clear. I'd listened to the egot! I didn't even realise I was doing it. The egot had suggested I pull Snotty McGill's hair. And I'd pulled her hair. Just like that! I hadn't even thought about it. I'd just done it; right there, right then, right away.

And I'd thought I'd shut the egot up! What a fool I'd been!

My blood froze and my muscles turned to rock.

That scream sliced the air clean in two.

Miss Grey's face was a portrait of disappointment; with art nouveau cheeks and minimalist eyes. Her dimples, which pulsated when she was happy, stiffened and then disappeared. The flowers on her summery dress seemed to wilt and fade.

"Sorry Miss," I whimpered. "I didn't mean to do it."

"So why did you do it then?" my teacher replied.

"Tell her the truth," the egot suggested. It looked far more comfortable than it had done before. It had regained some of its old *va va* voom. The glint had returned to its eye.

"Tell her what Snotty McGill did."

"*Shut up!*" I snapped back inside my head.

"I'm a naughty boy, Miss," I replied out loud. "I'm a very, very naughty boy. I deserve to be punished."

Miss Grey gazed into my eyes.

She looked so damn beautiful! There was a fire in her which turned her face red. And there was a softness in her too. I actually saw her visibly melt in front of me. Her shoulders relaxed. Her dimples reappeared.

"Do you really want to be punished?" she asked.

"Yes Miss," I replied. "I really, really want to be punished. I want to be punished so hard that I'll never act out like that again. I'm a bad, bad boy. I need you to teach me a lesson."

I could hear the egot's heart breaking:

'*Crack!!!*'

The egot clutched its chest and doubled over. It choked. Its golden hair turned a pale shade of grey.

I felt its pain. It was like a little part of me was suffering too. My chest felt tight and my throat constricted. An electric flush passed through me.

Miss Grey chuckled. Her dimples began to pulse.

"Okay," she said. "I'll tell you what; you can administer your own punishment. Write 'Hair Puller' on this piece of cardboard and use that piece of string to hang it from your neck. You can wear it as a sign of your remorse for however long you think is appropriate.

"Does that sound okay, my little lieutenant?"

I nodded.

I hung that sign from my neck and wore it for a full four weeks. Miss Grey had to remove it from me in the end. She said that I'd punished myself enough.

TEN

The egot whimpered each time I wore that sign. It clutched its ribs each time I ignored its advice. Its skin, which was once as red as hellfire, took on a dull and dusty hue. Its hair became an even paler shade of grey.

That's not to say that I didn't listen to the egot. Like in the previous story, there were occasions when I followed its advice instinctively. Those occasions were rare. They only took place every few months. But they did take place...

I listened to the egot when it suggested I pass a love note to Stacey Fairclough. I wrote; '*I love your hair. It looks really pretty*'. I didn't think about what I was doing. I just did it. Firstly, because it was something I genuinely wanted to do. And secondly, because it was true. Stacey's hair did look elegant. That girl was starting to bloom.

The egot glowed. Its skin glistened for the first time in weeks. And a few strands of its hair recovered their golden lustre.

But when Miss Grey took me off Cupboard Monitor duties, as a punishment for disrupting the class, and when I accepted that punishment without complaining, the egot regressed even further. It started to walk with a stoop. And it started to shed its hair.

During one particularly stressful lesson, in which our class had to recite multiplication tables out loud, I screamed '*Poo! Piss! Puke!*' at the top of my voice. The egot had crossed its legs, lit its pipe, and suggested that I do it. And I'd done it. Just like that, without even thinking. Although I suppose I had wanted to let off some steam.

The egot immediately regained a little of its strength. Its elfish ears picked up and its eye sparkled for the first time in over six months.

But Miss Grey didn't react so positively. Her dimples completely disappeared. Her summery dress hung limply from her narrow shoulders. And she made me sit in silence for a full three hours. Three hours!

My mum was also shocked when she found out what I'd done. Her face also turned ashen and gaunt. The love drained from her eyes. And she began to mutter:

"Why can't you be a good boy? Why do you insist on doing things I wouldn't do? Why, oh why, oh why?"

She stopped me from watching television for a week. She threw my favourite record in the bin. And she cancelled our monthly trip to the cinema.

I accepted all of those punishments.

And so the egot shrivelled. Its cheeks ended up looking like two stale raisins. Its spherical belly began to sag. Its claws began to fall out. And its body began to shrink.

Then there was the time when Miss Grey helped Gavin with his work. She leaned over us in such a way that her summery dress fell onto the desk in front of me.

I couldn't resist it. I couldn't restrain myself. I couldn't help but listen to the egot!

At its suggestion, I lifted my greedy hand and clenched that delicate cotton. I caressed it. I held it to my eyes and gazed at the image of a Viceroy butterfly. I even caught a glimpse of Miss Grey's thigh.

And, I must admit, it felt rather epic. My whole body filled with sordid bliss. My heart pounded with uncontrollable glee. And I grew by a full three inches.

The egot also grew in confidence. It also grew in size. It also smiled with uncontrollable glee.

But Miss Grey was screaming:

"Insurrection! Mutiny! Lieutenant Shodkin - know your place!"

Her look of shock and horror brought me crashing down to earth with a bone-shattering bump. Seeing her twisted neck and bulging mouth made me realise what I'd done. And I couldn't believe it. I couldn't believe I'd listened to the egot.

I was made to wear kitchen mittens for two weeks after that. They were hot and sweaty, itchy and coarse. They stank something chronic! But I never complained. Even though I didn't like it, I genuinely believed that I deserved that punishment.

And so the egot became even frailer. Its teeth fell out, its skin turned white and its body shrunk to half its original size.

The egot suffered whenever I accepted a punishment. And that happened a lot. Because, over the months which followed, I was punished whenever anything went wrong. Anything at all.

I was punished when my class's test results were poor, even though my own results were okay.

I was punished for flooding the toilets. But I didn't even do it! Honest to god! I don't know who was responsible, but it certainly wasn't me.

And I was punished for knocking over a pot of paint. It was an accident. An accident, I tell you! But I got punished for it nonetheless.

It was as if my teachers had a default setting; *'Something's gone wrong, let's blame Yew Shodkin'*.

I was guilty until proven innocent. And there wasn't ever a fair trial. My teachers were my judge, jury and executioner. I kneeled over and they put me to the sword.

I accepted it.

The egot writhed about in pain.

ELEVEN

The egot got smaller and frailer, weaker and meeker. Its feet lost their webbing and its elfish ears went limp. Its flat cap began to fray and its charm began to fade.

It became so pathetic that I was finally able to stop it at source.

It happened on one of those confusing days where the weather doesn't know if it's coming or going; swapping opulent horizons for ubiquitous fog; flicking between exultant sunshine and furious clouds.

Mrs Skellet, our teacher that year, was prattling on about some gory war in ancient Greece. The tyres of fat which encircled her belly were battling with her skirt's top button. And her perfume was fighting a losing battle with her fetid body odour. She smelled of overcooked chestnut soup.

I was distracted.

I didn't care much for stories of bloody battles or Trojan horses. So my eyes began to wander. I looked at each pupil in turn. And I thought about what they'd really like to be doing.

Snotty McGill was wrapped up in the lesson. Her beady eyes were transfixed on Mrs Skellet's spongy lips. So I imagined her as a pirate, swinging from a ship's mast, waging war like one of the fighters in Mrs Skellet's stories.

Stacey Fairclough was twiddling a lock of her hair; preening herself like a pompous peacock. So I imagined her as a supermodel, gliding down a catwalk whilst hundreds of cameras flashed away.

Chubby Smith was juggling his man-boobs. So I imagined him as a lion tamer, strutting his booty whilst holding out a hoop at arms-length.

He gave the lion a cheeky wink. Then it jumped through the hoop.

Sleepy Sampson was asleep.

I continued to scan the room until I saw something move, suddenly and skittishly, beneath a set of standing shelves.

I stared at that skeletal structure. My eyes were fixed on it.

But nothing happened.

Slow tick followed slow tock.

And then, in the blink of an eye, the school mouse shot out at full speed. It had broken free!

"Yippee!" the egot cheered, whilst clutching its ribs in pain. "Freedom! Yes, yes."

The mouse scuttled along the skirting board.

The egot tried to jump for joy. It didn't have the strength to catch any air, but its face did visibly brighten. The semblance of a smile formed on its leathery cheeks. And a sad flicker of hope appeared in its forlorn eyes. In *my* forlorn eyes.

The mouse shot towards the closed door.

"Let it out!" the egot cheered. It panted. It retched. It composed itself. And then it continued:

"Open the door! You want to help it escape! I think you do! Yes, yes."

And, you know what? I was about to do it! My chest jolted forwards. I leapt out of my seat!

But it's like Lao Tzu says; '*Recompenses follow good and evil, just as shadows follow substance*'.

Well, the '*substance*' of the egot's influence, which had propelled me forward, was followed by the '*shadow*' of my self-restraint, which held me back. Action met equal and opposite reaction. My ribs blocked the forward momentum of my innards. My knees locked. And my shoulders buckled.

My spine flipped back and my feet flew forwards. My body was held aloft by the lightness of the air. And my bum crashed down against the hardness of the floor.

My whole class laughed at me. <u>At</u> me! I knew they weren't laughing with me. I was sure of it.

I was so embarrassed. My face turned completely red.

The egot wasn't just red-faced. It was red all over! It was engulfed by a ball of smokeless fire. It glowed. It yelled. And it collapsed onto the floor of my occipital lobe, where it lay in a pile of its own cinders.

It looked up at me with utter desperation.

I looked down at it with utter contempt.

"I'm sorry," I said to Mrs Skellet.

I dusted myself down and returned to my seat.

"The school mouse has escaped," I continued. "We need to catch it and put it back in its cage."

TWELVE

The egot hardly spoke after that. I don't think it had the strength.

It looked like a burns victim, which I suppose it was. And it lived like a geriatric in a hospice. It hardly moved. It spent most of its time bathing in a pool of my cerebrospinal fluid. It was so thin you could see its skeleton. But its eyes were still identical to my own.

I think it still tried to influence me, but its little voice had become so quiet that I could barely hear it. My mind was clear. And so I stopped misbehaving. I finally became a good little boy. A respectable member of classroom society. I wrote inside the lines and everything!

I never talked unless I was spoken to. I never fought or played during class. I never stuck chewing gum on anyone else. Never! Not even once!

I took part in 'Homework Club', joined the school choir, and tried to get onto the school football team. (I didn't quite make it).

I always kept my shirt tucked in, my collar down and my shoes tied. I tried to keep my trousers clean. (I usually failed).

I made a bid to become the class prefect. (I came third in the vote).

But my grades picked up. I came second in my class in science. I came third in an egg and spoon race. And I was even a member of the winning team when our class had a bake off!

My conformity breathed life back into my dear old mother. Whenever she dropped me off at school, she'd still hug me, kiss me and say:

"Be a good boy. Don't do anything I wouldn't do!"

Her eyes still looked sincere. So honest! So loving!

But there was something new about her demeanour. Something

indescribable. Something like hope. Something like faith. It was as if she actually believed what she was saying; that she actually believed I might be a *'good boy'*; that I might not *'do anything she wouldn't do'*.

If you consider my transformation somewhat far-fetched, dear reader, or if it seems a little unrealistic, please do bear in mind that I have what psychologists call an 'All or Nothing' personality. I engage in a process called 'Splitting'.

I can eat a whole bag of chocolates, or I can refrain from eating any chocolates at all, but I can't just eat one chocolate and then close the box. I can't do moderation.

So when it came to behaving, if I was going to do it at all, I was going to do it fully. I was going to obey every single rule, no matter the circumstances. And I was going to look down on anyone who didn't do the same.

Let me give you a few examples of this sort of behaviour...

When I'd just turned ten my class was told to queue outside whilst our teacher went to find a colleague. Well, it started to rain, so all the other kids went inside. But I obeyed orders. I stood in the rain!

I started to shiver. I caught a cold. All my classmates thought I'd gone mad. Even Gavin Gillis, who was my best friend at the time, shook his head and tutted. Chubby Smith smirked like a chimpanzee. He gave me a cheeky wink.

But I was following the rules. I was proud of myself for that. And my teacher gave me a house point too, so I did feel vindicated in the end.

Another time, when my class was told off for not singing loudly enough in assembly, I sang so loudly that all the birds jumped off their branches! I totally drowned out the sound of every other child!

And then, aged eleven, my obedience actually got me into trouble.

It all started when I needed to go to the toilet:

"Please can I go for a pee-pee?" I asked.

"Why?" Mrs Balding, our teacher that year, replied.

"I need to pee."

"Really Yew! You should have gone at lunchtime!"

I bowed my head.

I wanted to say, '*I didn't need to go at lunchtime*', but I knew better than to answer back. Mrs Balding was nice, but she was strict. One time, she screamed at Chubby Smith because he winked at her! She made Gavin Gillis walk around barefoot all day because he had mud on his shoes!

So you really didn't want to get on Mrs Balding's bad side. Oh no! And answering back would have put me on her bad side. So I just sat there, crossing and uncrossing my legs. And, after several uncomfortable minutes, I was finally allowed to go.

"Really Yew! Is it an emergency?" Mrs Balding whined. Her hair, which looked like a bird's nest, seemed to visibly contract.

I nodded eagerly and ran out the room.

Well, by the time I returned 'Quiet Time' had already started. Everyone was sitting at their desks, reading or writing.

I liked the quiet. It allowed me to daydream.

I dreamt about running through the woods, with bracken between my toes and dry leaves in my hair. I dreamt about splashing about in a salivating ocean. I dreamt about flying through the clouds like a bird.

Sleepy Sampson started to hum.

It was unusual, because Sleepy Sampson usually slept through Quiet Time. And I felt that it was wrong, because you weren't supposed to hum. When I hummed during Quiet Time I was made to write lines; '*Silence is golden, hums should be held in'.*

I felt that I needed to do something. And so I held a finger over my lips and shushed Sleepy Sampson.

Sleepy Sampson stuck her tongue out. It was u-shaped and roseate.

I scowled.

Sleepy Sampson continued to hum. Her head rocked from side to side. It made her pigtails swing.

"It's quiet time," I whispered. "You're not supposed to hum during quiet time."

It was a strange thing. A strange thing indeed.

I, Yew Shodkin, breaker of rules and defender of freedoms, was telling someone else to conform! It was as if I'd become a totally different person; empty, generic and docile. But that's exactly what you get when you apply a process of Operant Conditioning to someone with an All or Nothing personality; a person who is just as extreme as before, but in the completely opposite way.

Sleepy Sampson was still humming. She looked happy. There was a smile on her cherry blossom cheeks. White light flickered in her eyes and a pinkish flush swept across her countenance.

"I'll tell Miss," I whispered.

I wouldn't have told our teacher. That was a hollow threat. And anyway, I couldn't have told our teacher without speaking, which wasn't allowed during Quiet Time. But I did want to stop Sleepy Sampson's humming. I thought I was protecting her from being punished.

Sleepy Sampson yanked my ear. She actually yanked my ear! Can you believe it?

She stretched her rangy arm across our table, grabbed hold of my earlobe, and yanked it down as hard as she could. It hurt something chronic. Stars and dots fizzled around my ear. My blood simmered and my veins pulsed.

But I didn't scream. It was Quiet Time. And you weren't supposed to scream during Quiet Time.

I just scowled at Sleepy Sampson, who was still humming, and I shushed her once more.

She kicked me. Honest to god. She actually kicked me! Her spiky toe ricocheted into my ankle. It pierced my delicate skin.

I winced. But I didn't react.

We'd all been told that the school had a 'Zero Tolerance' policy on fighting; that if two children fought they'd both be punished. The only way to avoid punishment was by refusing to fight, even if someone else was attacking you. You just had to stay calm and take the beating. Then the other person would be punished and you wouldn't.

Those were the rules. And you weren't supposed to break the rules.

So I took a deep breath, sucked up my pain, and scowled at Sleepy Sampson.

She threw her pen at me. I tell no lie. She actually threw her pen at me!

It was one of those inky fountain pens which all the pretentious girls used to use. I never saw the point in them myself; they always created a splodgy mess. So of course a shower of ink went all over the place. It sprayed blue rain all over my white shirt. And it even found its way into my mouth. It tasted alkaline; synthetic, oily and sour.

I scowled at Sleepy Sampson.

She threw her rubber at me. She threw her exercise book at me. She jumped over the table, grabbed my collar and pushed me back. My chair tipped over and dumped me onto the floor.

"You're not the boy we all used to love," she growled. "You're not the boy *I* used to love!"

Her right palm slapped my left cheek. Her left palm slapped my right cheek. She slapped me again and again; left, right, left, right; with the up-tempo beat of a hungry jackhammer.

The indignity of it! The indignity of being beaten up by a girl! A scrawny girl! A girl who spent most of her time asleep.

The shame of it stuck with me for years.

The egot writhed around in pain. It took every blow that came my way. But it couldn't withstand those blows like I could. Its cheeks were too frail. And so its cheekbones gradually inverted. They squeezed into its mouth and applied pressure to its brain. The egot's face became egg-shaped. Then it became pear-shaped. One of its eyes popped out, bounced off its belly, and rolled into a puddle of fluid.

The blows kept on coming.

Mrs Balding was coming too. She was rushing between tables and jinking between chairs. Her hair was clinging on for dear life.

"Really Sampson!" she screamed. "What do you think you're doing?

"Really Yew! What on earth did you do to provoke her?"

She lifted Sleepy Sampson off me.

"Really Yew!" she exclaimed. "I thought you'd put this sort of behaviour behind you."

My face was on fire. It was sore, itchy and red.

"What happened?"

I shivered.

"Speak to me!"

I looked up at Mrs Balding and whispered:

"I can't speak during Quiet Time."

"I'm asking you a question," my teacher snapped back. "Really Yew! Don't be so facetious."

I shook my head and locked my lips. There was no way I was going to break that rule.

"If you don't speak up, I'll put you on permanent detention!"

I didn't speak up. I just closed my eyes and looked inside myself.

I saw the egot.

The egot went through a series of deathly convulsions. Its muscles spasmed with horrific violence. It gurgled so much that white chalk bubbled out of its mouth. And it rasped for air in such a high-pitched manner that it made my head throb with anodic pain.

I didn't know what to feel.

The egot's right arm shot into its chest. Pop! Just like that. It completely disappeared.

The egot's left arm followed suit. Its right leg fell off. Its left leg went limp.

The egot looked up at me with hollow eyes. With *my* hollow eyes! And with its final breath, it said:

"Goodbye old friend. Just remember that I always had your best interests at heart. I always loved you. I only ever wanted you to be yourself."

THIRTEEN

The egot died. And then it decomposed. I had to walk around with its decaying body stinking up my brain for a full month. God it hurt! It felt like all of Caesar's horses were stampeding over my head, trampling my skull; with hooves which were eager to push me down and legs which were determined to crush me.

My head pulsated. My eyes watered and my brow turned dark purple.

The egot's rigor mortis gave way to a bloated sort of putrefaction. Its body expanded like a balloon; full of sordid gas and sublime desolation. Froth dripped from its nose, mouth and anus. Pus dripped from its empty eye-sockets.

My head throbbed like a speaker at a rave.

The egot's body crumbled. Its sallow skin turned to ash. Maggots devoured its bones. And my brain matter absorbed its remains.

My pain began to subside.

Then, one moody autumn evening, the last remnants of the egot finally blew away. My nostrils opened wide and sucked up the most glorious gulp of air I'd ever tasted. My lungs shook with pure excitement.

I felt an overwhelming sense of lightness.

I was finally free.

FOURTEEN

The autumn of my youth turned into the winter of my adolescence.

If one thing defined that period of my life, it'd have to be my subservience to authority. Without the egot by my side, I was simply incapable of challenging people in positions of power.

I didn't follow Lao Tzu's advice, to '*Respond intelligently to unintelligent treatment*'. I went along with whatever '*unintelligent treatment*' came my way.

It's not hard to understand why.

Years of Operant Conditioning had turned me into an obedient little automaton, like a rat in one of Skinner's experiments. I followed all the rules. I didn't need to be threatened or bribed. I just complied.

And I wasn't alone.

Subservience to authority is the norm in our society. This was shown by the social psychologist, Stanley Milgram...

Milgram conducted an experiment in which two people were given different roles. 'Mr Wallace', an actor who was playing the part of a volunteer, was placed in one room. Electrodes were attached to his arms. And a genuine volunteer was placed in the adjacent room. He faced a <u>fake</u> electric shock generator and thirty switches marked from '15 volts (Slight Shock)' to '375 volts (Danger!)' and '450 volts (XXX)'. The real volunteer thought they'd been chosen for that role at random, that they could have been in Mr Wallace's position, and that the electric shock generator was real.

Mr Wallace was asked to memorize a list of word pairs. Then, when he was ready, the volunteer was asked to test him; to give Mr Wallace one word and ask him to reply with the other word in the pair. Each time Mr Wallace made a mistake, the volunteer was asked to administrate an electric shock, the severity of which went up by one unit for each wrong answer.

I don't know what it is with psychologists and electric shocks. I think they're a little sadistic. But, fortunately, no rats were used in Milgram's experiment, which was a definite plus as far as I'm concerned.

Anyway, as the experiment progressed, it would become apparent to the volunteer that Mr Wallace was suffering. Each time he received a shock, that actor whimpered. When the voltage was increased, he began to writhe and yell. And when the voltage reached the highest levels, he screamed out in agony; emitting hellish wails and deathly shrieks.

If the volunteer asked to stop, an official-looking scientist said, 'Please continue'. If they expressed concern again, they were told that 'The experiment requires you to continue'. Then; 'It's absolutely essential that you continue'. And finally; 'You have no choice but to continue'.

The results were shocking.

Two-thirds of the volunteers continued all the way to the final level. They even continued when Mr Wallace pretended to be dead! Can you believe that? Two thirds of everyday people, people just like you and me, were prepared to kill an innocent man, just because a scientific experiment demanded it! Those people were more influenced by an authority figure, a scientist in formal attire, than they were by the deathly scream of a dying man.

It's not hard to see why.

Our society encourages us to obey authority. It's a matter of Operational Conditioning; we're rewarded when we follow authority's rules and punished when we break those rules. Slowly but surely, we're gently coerced into a state of total obedience.

Well, like the volunteers in Milgram's experiment, I'd been coerced into such a state. I'd have done anything an authority figure asked me to do. As long as they looked the genuine article, with a haughty title and a well-presented façade, I'd have obeyed them without a second thought.

That was the story of my teenage years.

They are not years which I wish to dwell on. I wouldn't want to bore you, dear reader, with lots of anecdotes which all highlight the same state of affairs. Having spent the first part of this book talking about my childhood, a period in which my elders took the wet clay of my personality and moulded it into the shape they desired, I wish to move on to talk about my early adulthood, when the effects of that manipulation hit home. But before I do that, I feel that I should give you a few brief examples of my subservience, just to demonstrate where I was at…

Like the volunteers in Milgram's experiment, who did whatever the scientist told them to do, I believed everything my teachers told me, even when they were lying.

When they told me that Christopher Columbus had discovered the Americas, I believed them. I didn't think to ask about the people who'd been living there for tens of thousands of years. I didn't think to study the Vikings, who'd made the journey five hundred years before Columbus, or the Africans, who'd been making that journey for centuries. ('*Trading in gold-tipped spears*' according to Columbus's very own journal). I didn't think at all. I just accepted what I was told.

I accepted that we had once had a '*Great Empire*' which had '*Civilised*' the world. I accepted that we had defeated the evil communists and fascists. I was oblivious to the fact that we'd killed millions of people in the process, invented concentration camps, and pushed opium onto the Chinese. That sort of stuff was brushed under the carpet.

My teachers told me that the ancient Egyptian civilisation was founded by white people, despite all the hard evidence which proves it was founded by black people. They told me that paper and printing were Western inventions, when in fact they were developed in China. And they told me that Galileo discovered the movements of the planets, even though scholars in Timbuktu knew about them two centuries before.

I believed it all. I devoured that propaganda without thinking twice. Without thinking at all. It made me feel good to believe that the majority of human advancements had been made by white men, just like myself. That kind of patriarchal white-supremacism really swelled my ego.

Well, my whole education was tinged with historical misrepresentations like those. Historical misrepresentations which justified the status quo. Historical misrepresentations which *glorified* the status quo. And which, therefore, helped to maintain the status quo.

It's like George Orwell said; '*He who controls the past, controls the present. And he who controls the present, controls the future*'.

Well, my teachers were trying to control my future. But they weren't at it alone. Oh no! My parents were at it too!

Like my teachers, my parents were authority figures. The law gave them 'Parental Rights and Responsibilities', including the right to administer punishments. And their religion commanded; '*Honour your father and mother. Then you will live a long, full life*'.

I wanted to live a '*Long, full life*'.

So when my parents asked me to perform a 'Coming of Age' ceremony, to confirm my dedication to *their* religion, I was inclined to acquiesce. They were authority figures, after all, and I was just a subservient little boy. What choice did I have?

However, a small part of me wasn't so sure.

It's hard to explain. It wasn't as if the egot had returned. I wasn't being pushed to refuse or rebel. But I did feel a nagging. A dull, gentle, element of doubt, which pulsated beneath the surface of my conscious mind, and asked; *'Do I really want to do this? Do I really want glorify my parents' vicious, egotistical god? A god who inflicts disease, war and famine upon his people? A god who judges us like a crazed dictator? A god of Operant Conditioning, who bribes us with heaven and threatens us with hell?'*

So I raised my concerns during a family dinner, in-between mouthfuls of gravy-drenched roast potatoes and salty green beans.

I didn't refuse, please understand. That would have been naughty. And I was a good little boy. My rebellious days were behind me.

But I did express my discomfort:

"I don't really think I want to do the ceremony," I said. "You know, if that's okay with you."

My family were aghast.

My dad's chin jutted forward.

My mum said:

"Oh Yew! My angel! Be a good boy. Please be a good boy."

And my favourite cousin took into my uncle's study for a chat:

"Think of all the presents you'll receive," he told me. "People you've never even heard of will give you money! You'll get more gifts than you've ever been given before. It'll be the biggest payday of your life!"

We returned to the dinner table.

My grandma scowled at me.

God I loved my grandma! For me, she was like a portal into another time. A lavender scented goddess. Maternal. She always gave me chocolates and ice-cream. She always smiled when she saw me.

But she wasn't smiling then.

"You won't be my grandson if you don't perform the ceremony," she said. "I'll disown you! No grandson of mine would choose not to do it."

I froze, like a deer in the headlights.

My lips turned to wood.

My dad's chin jutted forwards.

Well, dear reader, I suppose it'd be easy for you to consider this a case of Operant Conditioning. After all, I was being bribed with rewards (the gifts), and I was being threatened with a punishment (disownment).

But by that stage in my life, I didn't need to be threatened or punished. I just needed to be shown that the issue was serious. That was all.

My whole persona had already been coerced. My fear of being punished was so great that I didn't need to be threatened. My imagination filled the gaps. I imagined far worse punishments than being disowned by my gran. I imagined being disowned by my whole family. I imagined being banned from family dinners, trips and holidays. I imagined being ignored; as if I was invisible; as if I didn't even exist.

I was weak. I was like a boxer on the ropes, pummelled within an inch of his life by a far superior fighter. I couldn't stand up for myself. All I could do was move my head, in a vain attempt to soften the blows.

"My dear Yew!" my mother repeated. "Please be a good boy."

And I listened to her. I *did* behave like a good boy. I obeyed my family, just like Milgram's volunteers had obeyed the scientist.

I did it because it was clearly important to my family. It was something I was clearly supposed to do. And that was enough. I didn't need to be threatened. I didn't need to be bribed. I just needed to be told. That selfless urge of mine, that deep need to please others, took over and did the rest.

I went to a religious service for three hours each week. I went to an evening-school twice a week. And I celebrated every religious festival which came my way.

After two years, I finally performed my Coming of Age ceremony.

Although I don't think my parents ever appreciated it. They never said 'thank-you'. I think they just took it for granted that I'd do as they pleased; that I'd be deferential. They were authority figures, after all. I was *supposed* to do everything they wanted. I was *supposed* to be a good boy. They didn't consider it a big deal.

Anyway, that all happened when I was about twelve or thirteen. And there's just one other event which I'd like to mention at this juncture; an event which took place when I was about to turn sixteen.

I had to make a decision which would shape my entire future:

'*Should I find a job?*'

'*Should I do an apprenticeship?*'

'*Perhaps I should do a vocational course?*'

'*Perhaps I should set up a business?*'

'*Maybe I should live a self-sufficient life out in the country?*'

'*Or maybe I should continue on at school and then go to university?*'

I liked the idea of living a self-sufficient life. Of getting close to Mother Nature. Of living like my ancestors had lived.

But, for my parents, there was only one option. I was going to stay on at school, whether I liked it or not. My indoctrination was going to continue.

"You're going to university," my dad told me. He was sitting behind his leather-coated desk, looking like a real boss; with his poncy suit and his smug sense of superiority. He looked sly. Vicious. His chin jutted forwards and his eyebrows jumped for joy.

"If you go to university, I'll support you," he continued. "You won't have to worry about paying for bills or fees, food or accommodation.

"But if you leave school I'll kick you out. You won't be welcome in *my* house anymore. You'll have to fend for yourself, out there in the big bad world."

Rewards and threats!

Rewards and threats!

I didn't feel like I had a choice. I was petrified of being homeless. I imagined myself lying beneath the sweaty arches of a busy train station, covered in soot, with worms in my pockets and ants in my hair. I imagined myself being mugged, beaten and raped, on a regular basis.

And I also thought about my father. I felt a duty to stay on in education for him. It clearly meant a lot to him. And I did want to make him happy. I really did believe that staying on at school would make him pleased. I dreamed that it would make him smile and say 'Thank-you'.

I think I must have had 'Stockholm Syndrome'.

So I stayed on at school and I went to university. Not because I wanted to, please understand. Not because I saw any benefit in it. I did it because authority figures expected me to do it. My parents and my teachers expected me to do it. My society expected me to do it. That's what middle class white boys were supposed to do. And so I did it. I did it for them. It was selfless. It was subservient.

I spent another five years in the school system that had stifled me so much already. I was rejected by my first choice university, so I went to one which I didn't really like. And I attended most of my lectures.

I was told; *'This is the scientific truth - there's no point questioning it'*. *'This theory holds true if we assume A, B and C'*. And, *'You can read about alternative points of view - but they won't be on the exam'*.

I learned how to argue. They called it 'Debate'. I learned how to worship. I learned how to become an eager worker and a passive consumer.

But I didn't learn anything practical, like how to purify water, build a home, start a fire, grow food, or survive without the help of corporations.

I smiled. I pretended to be happy. I told myself that other people were worse off than I was. I mean, I had food and shelter, after all. Some people didn't even have that. Who was I to complain?

I made the best of a bad situation.

I even got myself my first ever real girlfriend, Georgie; a feisty lass who had a sharp intellect and an even sharper tongue. She wore perfume which was moreish beyond belief, and clothes which had a casual sort of elegance. Her hair was luxurious and her skin felt like silk.

I almost felt happy when I was with Georgie. I got butterflies in my stomach whenever I saw her. Sometimes she'd say things which really resonated. Things which gave me goose-pimples.

We breathed in time when we slept.

Yeah, Georgie was great. She made me feel like a real human-being. She really helped me through those ambivalent years. I thought she was 'The One'.

I made friends at university too. We stayed in touch after we'd graduated.

And I actually did quite well. I guess it was down to my All or Nothing Personality. Even though I didn't want to go to university, I did want to succeed whilst I was there. I was 'All In'.

But I don't think my parents ever appreciated the sacrifices I'd made for them. My dad did give me some money, as a reward for doing well. That was nice. I appreciated the thought. But it was a reward for doing well. It wasn't a 'thank-you' for going in the first place. My dad never said 'thank-you' for going to university. Never. Not even once.

My mum was also pleased with me for getting good grades:

"Oh Yew!" she cheered. "You're such a good boy. I'm so proud of you, my angel. You've exceeded my expectations!"

But she didn't say 'thank-you' for going to university either.

That hurt. It hurt so much. I felt like I'd been stabbed in my chest with a rusty dagger. Like someone had ripped my heart out and kicked it through an open window.

I gave those people five years of my life! Five years!

Well, that betrayal took its toll. It really stretched our relationship. We still saw each other every now and again. But there was no warmth. No love. Not much of anything at all.

A massive chasm opened up between us.

We just sort of drifted apart.

FIFTEEN

I was told at school that I should stay on in school. Funny that. My teachers said my life would be better if I got an education. They said it'd help me to get a good job.

But it didn't.

I never got a good job, even though I applied for hundreds of graduate positions. I was never rewarded for my hard work.

Of course, I put my university degree at the top of my CV. I made a big deal about my grades whenever I had an interview. But my interviewers never seemed that interested. They always stuck to the questions which had been pre-approved by management:

'Where do you see yourself in five years?'

'What would you say were your biggest strengths and weaknesses?'

'What three items would you want if you were stuck on a desert island?'

'If you could be any animal, which animal would you be?'

'Why are manhole covers round?'

I wasn't any good at those interviews.

They say that interviewers judge you within the first few seconds of making your acquaintance. If you make a good first impression, you stand a good chance of getting the job, regardless of how well you do in the interview itself. Regardless of your qualifications or work experience.

Unfortunately, I've never been able to make good first impressions. I'm not attractive enough to wow people with my looks. I don't have enough charm to weasel my way into their good books. And I look awkward when I try to mirror their body language.

Yeah, you're supposed to do that. Psychologists say it helps to build rapport. But that sort of thing has always made me feel uncomfortable. It's always made me feel dishonest.

So, after five years in further education, with an overdraft which was growing by the day, I was left with no choice but to take a job in a call centre. I became a charity fundraiser.

Georgie, meanwhile, got a much better job. She left me and moved in with a more successful man. And I can't say that I blame her; her life was going places and mine clearly wasn't. But being dumped like that did leave me feeling low. My skin stretched taut. It made my skull feel like it was being crushed.

I spent night after night crying into my pillow. As soon as I stopped crying, I began to feel angry. I punched my pillow, over and over again; '*Bish! Bash! Bosh!*' And then I began to feel lonely. I hugged my pillow as if it was my partner.

Yeah, my pillow took a hell of a beating during those weeks.

I went on the rebound. I had a fling with the girl who sat next to me at work, Steph. She was nice; her eyes were like slices of kiwi and her mouth was like a segment of plum. But we didn't have much in common. Our relationship was intensely physical, but Steph never gave me goose-pimples like Georgie did. My heart never missed a beat when I saw her. And, although I'm not proud of it, I did resent her for holding the same position as me, even though she hadn't earned any formal qualifications.

Anyway, I digress. I was talking about my job...

It'd be wrong to say that my job was bad. It paid enough for me to get by, working conditions were safe, and I got along with my colleagues. But it'd also be wrong to say that my job was good. It didn't pay well enough for me to buy a flat, the work was tedious, and the system creaked under the weight of a million bullshit rules.

You had to sign in when you arrived. You were fined an hour's wages if you wore odd socks. If there was a logo on your shirt, you had to cover it up with tape. If you were unshaven you were made to shave with a one-blade razor. If you wanted to eat a banana you had to cut it into slices, so it wouldn't look like you were performing a sexual act. There was a strict *'No sex in the conference room'* rule which everyone had to obey.

You weren't allowed to say the word 'problem', only the word 'challenge'. We didn't have 'Bosses', we had 'Team Leaders'. Anyone who didn't donate was called a 'Future Donor' or a 'Yet To Give'. We couldn't 'Brainstorm', because it sounded too dangerous. We had to have 'Idea Showers' instead. We were told to take a 'holistic, cradle-to-grave' approach to our work. We had to use abstract concepts like 'Incentivisation', '360 degree thinking' and 'Pre-preparation'.

If you were in the middle of a call at the end of your shift you had to stay late to finish it, but you weren't compensated for your time. You had to take breaks, whether you wanted to or not, but you didn't get paid for them. The company changed your shifts whenever it liked.

And then there was the work itself.

I had to persuade the supporters of different charities to donate money each month via Direct Debit. If they already gave by Direct Debit, I had to encourage them to increase the size of their donations.

I loved the concept. I loved the idea of raising lots of money for good causes. I thought I'd be helping to make the world a better place; to end poverty, protect the environment, and advance the rights of abused minorities. Yeah, I genuinely believed that I'd be contributing to society.

I do think I did make a difference. A small difference, but a difference nonetheless. I channelled my selfless urges in a productive way.

But it would be false to say that everything was rosy.

I sat at a set of desks which I shared with five other fundraisers. The waxy floor was illuminated by white light. The smell of pencil shavings wafted through the air.

That prefabricated office reminded me of the school I attended as a child. But I didn't consider that to be a bad thing. I didn't feel the effects of my Nature Deficit Disorder like I had done at school. I actually felt at home in that office. That place felt familiar. I'd been in places like that for so long that they'd become the norm for me. It was almost as if my time at school had prepared me for that sort of environment.

Well, I'd sit in that office every day, making call after call:

"Hi," I'd say. "This is Yew calling from Charity X. Is that Mrs Jones?"

"Yes, who's this?" Mrs Jones would normally reply. Mrs Jones tended to be a frail pensioner, with a broken voice and a kind but vulnerable heart.

"It's Yew from Charity X," I'd repeat.

"Ooo," Mrs Jones would coo with an eager sort of trepidation. "Charity X! Oh yes, I like Charity X. They do a lot of good work with Issue Y."

"I'm glad you think that! Do you know what sort of things they do with Issue Y?"

"I heard they do Thing A."

"Yeah, they sure do! And they also do Thing B, Thing C and Thing D! They're out there every day, doing everything they can to tackle Issue Y. And do you know what?"

"What?"

"It's working, Mrs Jones! I tell no lie; it's making a real difference. You know, Charity X helped to reduce the effects of Issue Y by ten percent last year. It's true! A full ten percent!"

"Ooh. That's nice."

"And they did it thanks to people like you, Mrs Jones. Without your support they'd be nothing."

"Well I don't know about that. But I do what I can."

Mrs Jones tended to sound a little unsure by this point in the conversation. Her voice tended to shimmer with doubt. Her words tended to sound hollow.

"Now, now," I'd reassure. "Don't put yourself down Mrs Jones. You make a real difference. A real difference! But, alas, it's not *quite* enough."

"Not enough? Whatever do you mean?"

"Well, our forecasts show that if we don't act soon, Issue Y could grow by a hundred percent next year. It could double! And so that's why we're calling. We need *your* help, Mrs Jones. You can make the difference!"

Mrs Jones would sound wary when she replied to that comment. Sometimes she stammered. Sometimes she sputtered:

"That's a terrible situation," she would say. "But I honestly don't see how I could help. I'm just a little old lady."

"Oh, but you can help Mrs Jones," I'd reassure. "You really can! You see, Charity X needs to re-double their efforts to tackle the real and present dangers posed by Issue Y. But first, it needs to double its 'Battle Fund'. And that's why we're calling you; to ask if you'd be kind enough to double your monthly donation. It'll help Charity X to double their work!"

"I don't know about that," Mrs Jones would reply. Her voice would crackle. It'd break. It'd go coarse.

"I'm a pensioner you see. I don't have any spare money. And I do donate to Charity X already."

"You do Mrs Jones. And it's really appreciated. Your donations are making a real difference. They're really helping us to tackle the problems caused by Issue Y. But, unfortunately, it's not *quite* enough. If we're going to beat Issue Y, once and for all, then we're going to need you to *participate* a little more."

"'Participate' a little more?"

"Donate a little more."

"I don't have a little more."

"Oh, but Mrs Jones, you do! You really do! You just need to save a bit here and scrimp a bit there. Turn off your heating to save money on your electricity bill. Take a shower instead of a bath to reduce your water bill. Dig for victory! Scrimp and save! Then you'll be able to double your donation. Just like that! Easy peasy, lemon squeazy! You'll be able to help us to really tackle Issue Y."

"I'm not sure I could make those savings. I don't take baths."

"You can do it, Mrs Jones. You can do it! I believe in you."

"Aww, you're such a sweet young man."

"Thank-you Mrs Jones."

"But I can't afford to double my donation."

By this point in the conversation, Mrs Jones would normally sound more secure. More cocksure. She'd have rediscovered the courage of her convictions. Her confidence.

I was good at taking advantage of that confidence. I'd concede to it. I'd let Mrs Jones feel that she had beaten me down:

"I know, I know," I'd say. "Times are tough and you're already doing a lot. I understand. So how about we do things on your terms? Mrs Jones, do you think you'd be able to increase your monthly donation by just twenty percent? Do you think you'd be able to afford that?"

"Well, yes, I suppose I could afford that. That does sound more reasonable."

"Well then, I'll just set that up for you now!"

I'd hang up, tick a few boxes and call someone else.

God knows whatever happened to all the Mr and Mrs Joneses we called. We never did find out.

SIXTEEN

I was good at my job. I wasn't the best fundraiser, but I was far from the worst. I usually found myself in the top five of the leader-board which ranked us according to the 'sales' we'd made.

That made me feel proud. It made me feel warm and cosy.

I needed to be good. Fundraisers who didn't meet their targets weren't 'offered any more work'. They weren't sacked, as such, they just stopped being employed.

But I'm not sure that my success ever made me happy. It's not that it made me unhappy, please understand. It's just that I didn't really feel anything at all. I suppose you could say I was apathetic.

Gone were the highs. Beethoven never provided a soundtrack for my soul. My heart never surged and my adrenaline never pumped.

And gone were the lows; the punishments; the dread, pain and fear.

I think it was the egot's absence which bred that apathy.

You may have noticed that I haven't mentioned the egot during the last few pages. And that may seem strange to you. The first half of my story totally revolved around that character, and now it's completely disappeared. I've barely mentioned it. Perhaps that seems odd. Peculiar. Inconsistent. Perhaps it's left you feeling a little unfulfilled.

But the truth is that the egot didn't play a role in my adult life. I barely thought of it. I pretty much forgot that it had ever existed. I never heard its little voice. And that's why the egot is absent in these chapters.

Well, when the egot died it took my dissidence with it. My free-spirit. It took my ability to break free from my shackles. My ability to feel like I was on top of the world. And it also took the crushing pain I felt whenever

I was reprimanded and punished. The anxiety and distress. It took the highs *and* the lows.

I was left with an extreme sort of neutrality. A sort of neutrality which sucked every ounce of life from my being. But a sort of neutrality which, at the same time, also pretended to be my friend. I was grateful for it. I was grateful for being able to get by, steadily, without ever experiencing any emotional extremes such as elation or euphoria, despair or fear.

That neutrality bred a certain sort of numbness within me.

Days merged into weeks and weeks merged into years. The present ate the past and then excreted the future. I literally killed time; lining up coloured sweets on my phone, reading trashy stories, and completing the daily Sudoku. Putting a 'nine' in this box and a 'two' in that one.

Every day was the same.

I spent an hour getting ready for work, an hour travelling to work, nine hours at work, and an hour travelling home. By the time I got back, I'd be so tired that I'd just eat my dinner, watch some dumbed-down television and browse the internet. I'd fall asleep. Then I'd wake up and repeat the whole process again the next day.

Living that way helped me to fit in. Everyone in our office seemed to have similar lifestyles. We all walked around like zombies; with emptiness in our eyes and lethargy in our motions. We all seemed to conform.

This sort of conformity is actually pretty normal. There was a psychologist called Solomon Asch who studied it.

Asch performed an experiment in which a volunteer sat around a table with seven other people. The volunteer believed that those people were also volunteers, but they were actually actors. Psychologists are sneaky like that.

Well, the eight participants were given two cards at a time. The first card had one straight line printed on it. The other card featured three lines of different lengths; marked 'A', 'B' and 'C'.

The participants were then asked which one of those three lines was the same length as the line on the first card. The answer was always obvious. So, in the trials where everyone gave their honest opinion, they pretty much always gave the correct answer.

But then the actors started to give incorrect answers. On some occasions, they all gave the same incorrect answer.

The volunteer, who only spoke after all the actors had responded, was faced with a choice; to give the correct answer or the popular answer.

So what happened?

About three quarters of the volunteers went along with the actors and gave an incorrect answer. Three quarters! That's what happened!

When they were asked why they'd given those answers, most of the volunteers said it was because they didn't want to be ridiculed for being 'peculiar'; they'd wanted to fit in. This is called 'Normative Influence'. But some volunteers said that they'd actually believed the other participants had been correct! They'd thought those people had been better informed than them. This sort of conformity is called 'Informational Influence'.

Well, like those volunteers, I didn't want to seem peculiar. I didn't want to be ridiculed. And I did want to fit in. So I allowed Normative Influence to steer my behaviour.

And, at the same time, Informational Influence affected me too. I assumed, tacitly, that the way in which my peers behaved was the correct way to behave. I assumed that they knew something I didn't know. So I did things which weren't rational, things which I didn't really want to do, simply because other people were doing those things. I assumed that there must have been *some* sort of merit in it, even though I couldn't see it myself.

I walked around my section every day, offering to make all my teammates a cup of tea or coffee. I didn't do it because I wanted to. Most of the time I didn't even want a drink myself. I did it because that was the sort of thing my peers did, so I thought that I should do it too.

I started going to the gym, to put on some muscle, so I wouldn't stand out for being scrawny. I started to wear the same sort of clothes that everyone else wore. And I started to eat the same branded junk food that everyone else ate.

I started to listen to popular music; the generic, plastic tripe which mainstream radio stations play on repeat. I watched boring shows on TV, so I could speak about them at work the next day. And I made inane small-talk about celebrities, sport and the weather.

Looking back at those conversations now, I can't help thinking of the Lao Tzu proverb; '*He who knows does not speak. He who speaks does not know*'.

Well, I didn't '*know*' what I was talking about back then. And so I '*spoke*' a lot. A hell of a lot! I made a real effort to chat with each of my colleagues every single day.

I suppose it was like I was applying Operant Conditioning to myself. I created a reward, 'Fitting In', which I received whenever I acted like everyone else. And I created a punishment, 'Being a Social Outcast', which I would have experienced had I acted naturally.

I policed myself.

I was my own Skinner! My own jailor! My own worst enemy!

Those imagined punishments and rewards influenced me so much that I'd have done anything to fit in. Anything! Anything at all.

And, gradually, I think it had an effect...

Some of the other fundraisers invited me to the pub each Friday after work. I didn't like the pub, or the beer, but I did like being a part of that group. It made me feel wanted. And, it meant that I had three groups of friends. Three! Not just one. Three! There were my school friends (I still saw Gavin Gillis and Amy McLeish on a regular basis), my university friends and my work friends. I was denying my true self, but I was becoming really popular. That did cheer me up.

I started to see my work friends on our days off. Every now and again I went to their houses. Occasionally, we went to a gig or a football match together. That made me feel included. It helped me to get by.

The monotony of my job began to grate. And my doubts about my work began to grow. But I remained with that firm because I felt like I belonged there. I felt like I was one of the lads.

And, as time went by, I forgot that I didn't like eating that unnatural food or wearing those generic clothes. The rubbish TV actually comforted me. And the small-talk stopped feeling so inane.

I didn't think about those things. They were just things I did. Robotically. Systematically. As part of an unquestioned routine.

I became a new person; sucked into the neutrality of the abyss, comforted by social norms, and set free from the burden of individuality.

SEVENTEEN

I was smashing my targets, getting loads of old grannies to donate money they didn't really have.

My bosses liked that.

They gave the impression that they were thinking of promoting me. Well, they asked me about my aspirations and spoke to me about life as a 'Team Leader'. Then they invited me out for a night on the town.

I didn't feel I could say 'no'. I didn't say 'no' to authority figures. I was a good boy. Plus, I did genuinely want to fit in. I did want to conform.

So I joined them on their night out. I tried to behave like those managers; to speak like them and act like them.

We started off in a pub. It was one of those tired old pubs where people go to drink for the sake of drinking; replete with the aroma of stale beer and the soggy fug of drunken old men.

I didn't like drinking for the sake of drinking. But everyone was downing pint after pint, so I felt that I should too. I thought it'd help me to fit in.

Then we went to a casino. I'd never been to a casino before. I'd always thought they were silly. I mean, the house always wins! You just give them your money. It's a pretty ridiculous thing to do.

But I wanted to assimilate. I wanted to fit in. And so I sat down at the blackjack table, placed the minimum bet on each hand, and pretended to enjoy myself:

"I could get used to this," I lied to Mr Morgan, our chief executive.

Mr Morgan reminded me of Mr Grunt. Perhaps it was because of his straggly eyebrows. Or perhaps it was because of his forced joviality. But there was something about Mr Morgan. Something subtle. Something violent. He had the air of a stockbroker and the aura of an executioner.

Well, we were getting on well until I stuck on a fourteen.

"What did you do that for?" Mr Morgan lambasted. "Yew Shodkin. Yewy Shodkin! You're clearly not a team player."

That hurt. It made my stomach drop like a lead weight; thumping against my abdomen and pulling down on my lungs. It hurt because I was doing everything I could to be seen as a team player. And it hurt because I didn't have a clue what Mr Morgan was talking about. I didn't even realise that blackjack was a team game.

Anyway, despite that incident, I was still invited to the following managers' night out. And I was invited to the one after that as well.

Those outings took place every few months. They never helped me to get a promotion, but they did lead me to believe that a promotion was just around the corner. They made me feel like I was doing some good legwork.

On about the fourth or fifth such outing we started off in our usual pub. Then we walked towards the casino.

On the way, one of the directors, a guy who was simply known as 'Deano', had an idea. He was a messy man, that Deano. He had a foul mouth which was always full of blackberries and blasphemies. And he was always having crazy ideas:

"Hey lads!" he cheered with the exuberance of an inebriated clown. "Let's go in this fucking place! Hell yeah, my bitches!"

We were standing outside a topless bar.

A bouncer was guarding the door. He looked like the offspring of a bulldog and a penguin. To his side, a poster was advertising 'Naked Midgets'. And above his head, some garish red lights were screaming out,

'Girls! Girls! Girls!'

"Titties!!!" screamed Mr Clough, the Head of Accounts; a tubular man who had a barrel-shaped torso and baguette-shaped legs. "Boobies! Boobies! Boobies!"

It took me by surprise. In my experience, accountants don't normally shout the word 'boobies' out at the top of their voice. Not in a public.

"Let's get ourselves some snatch!" cheered Mr Smith, the red-faced Head of Human Relations.

"Oggy! Oggy! Oggy!" another manager chanted.

"Oi! Oi! Oi!" his buddy replied.

They high-fived.

I felt that I should join in.

"Naked girls!" I shouted. "You've gotta' love naked girls!"

"That's the spirit," Mr Morgan replied. He smiled with glee. A contorted, vicious sort of glee. And he put his arm around my shoulder. He led me inside.

"Come on Yewy," he said. "We'll have a hell of a time, dear boy!"

That place was like hell itself. The space around me was pitch black. I felt myself melt away into a blanket of its nothingness. And yet red lights blared from every surface. They imbued everything with a hellish glow. They made my eyes water.

I stumbled on and soon found myself in a u-shaped booth.

I downed a tequila and looked up at the stripper on stage.

Her body was, by any normal standards, a thing of beauty. Her moves were, in their own way, sublime. And yet I didn't find that girl alluring. I wouldn't have even said that she was sexy. Her eyes were empty. Her moves were robotic.

We all downed another tequila.

Mr Morgan looked my way. His straggly eyebrows merged. They looked like a wiry bush. And his elephantine skin crumpled into folds.

"Yew," he cheered. "Yewy Shodkin! You're single. Why don't you have a dance?"

I cringed. My muscles clenched. My stomach felt tight; as if all the air had been sucked out of it. As if it was nothing more than a shrivelled sack.

"It's not really my thing," I said.

I looked down at the floor in order to avoid eye-contact.

"Don't be silly," Mr Morgan replied. "Come! Come! Consider it my treat. You deserve it! You've been doing some great work."

Mr Morgan beckoned a girl toward us. He passed her a handful of folded notes. And then he nodded at me.

The girl took my hand and led me into a private room, where she sat me down on a hard, fabric-covered bench.

She swayed from side to side. She massaged her breasts. She licked her finger in a seductive manner.

That whole experience had a profound effect on me.

Please do allow me to explain...

You may recall the feeling I said I had when I was told to do a religious ceremony. Turn back a few pages and you'll see it, right there in chapter fourteen:

'A small part of me wasn't so sure', I wrote. 'It wasn't as if the egot had returned. I wasn't being pushed to refuse or rebel. But I did feel a nagging. A dull, gentle, element of doubt, which pulsated beneath the surface of my conscious mind, and asked; 'Do I really want to do this?''

Well, dear reader, I felt that same 'nagging' whilst I sat there in that strip club. I felt that same 'element of doubt'. I asked myself; 'Do I really *want to do this? Do I really want to degrade this poor young woman?'*

She was really going through the motions; squatting up and down, thrusting her pelvis towards my groin. But all I could see was an exploited little girl. Someone's daughter! Someone's lover! Someone's friend!

I wondered about her life.

Perhaps she was a student, I thought, who was trying to pay her way through university. Perhaps she was a single mum, doing everything she could to provide for her child. Or perhaps she was a slave, a victim of a people-trafficking mafia, who wasn't getting paid anything at all.

My imagination ran wild.

But, despite dreaming up scenario after scenario, I couldn't imagine a single situation in which that girl was happy. She was dangling her breasts in my face, but she didn't look like she was enjoying it. She was staring, blank-faced, at the wall behind me. She looked bored. She looked pissed-off.

I felt terrible.

I felt like a mangy dog. A rabid, flee-infested, mongrel bitch. An indignant mutt.

That dull thudding which pulsated beneath the surface of my mind began to throb. It made my stomach feel queasy.

But I didn't want to rebel. I wanted to conform. I wanted to fit in. That was why I'd gone out with those managers. It was why I'd allowed the stripper to lead me into that room. My conformity made me feel safe. It made me feel comfortable. It made me feel secure.

But my managers weren't in that room. Nothing I did in there could please or offend them. Nothing I did in there would help me to conform.

I really didn't want that dance to continue. I felt that I was abusing that poor innocent girl.

So I tapped the seat beside me.

"Sit down," I told the stripper.

And I gave her my jumper, so she could cover her naked chest.

We sat there in silence. Then we returned to the main room.

"That was quick," Mr Morgan said. "Everything okay, Yewy, dear boy?"

I shrugged.

I wanted Mr Morgan to appreciate the sacrifice I'd made for him. I really, really wanted him to be pleased. But he didn't seem grateful at all. He looked like he wanted me to be grateful *to him*!

He scowled at me. He actually scowled at me! His scraggly eyebrows stood on end!

My heart sunk. My stomach turned. And I ran to the toilet, where I was sick all over the floor.

EIGHTEEN

I lost my job.

My company went through a lean spell, during which time there simply wasn't enough work to go around. Everyone who didn't have experience of working for charities in Sector C was 'let go'.

"It's stupid," Mr Collins told me. "You're one of the best fundraisers here. There's no way we should be releasing you."

But they did '*release*' me. That's bureaucracy for you.

I didn't let it get me down though. No. My track record of success had boosted my ego. I was confident that I'd be a success in whatever job I was given. And that confidence shone through at interview. It helped me to get a new job within a month, working as a junior chef in the kitchen of a chain pub; microwaving pre-made meals and washing cheap china plates. It wasn't much; I was on a zero-hour contract, on the minimum wage. But it helped me to pay the bills.

I even got myself a new girlfriend, Lorraine; an older woman who had a cherubic face and mischievous eyes. We were good for each other. We both saw the world in a similar way. We both had our issues.

Lorraine and I moved in together after we'd been dating for a few months. That was a big step for me. It made me feel like an adult. Normal. Responsible.

And we got along. We stayed up late each night; drinking wine and putting the world to rights. We visited each other's friends. We went to the theatre together.

Yeah, I really did feel a placid sort of contentment when I was with Lorraine. It's not that I felt happy. I've already explained that I was living in a state of complete and utter apathy. But I did feel hopeful. I believed that things were on the up.

To understand my state of mind, it's first necessary to understand what the psychologist Tali Sharot calls the 'Optimism Bias'. It's the tendency, which most of us have, to overestimate the likelihood of experiencing good events and underestimate the likelihood of experiencing bad events.

In the Western World, for example, about two out of five married couples get divorced. Yet when newlyweds are told this and then asked about the likelihood of *them* getting divorced, they don't say there's a two in five chance. They don't give the rational answer. They say there's a zero percent chance. Zero! Zilch! Nada! Those people ignore the facts and let optimism cloud their judgement.

Likewise, a study by Neil Weinstein found that students thought they were 13% more likely than their classmates to receive an award, 32% less likely to suffer from lung cancer, and 49% less likely to get divorced. In reality, of course, their average chances would've been equal to the average chances of their peers. Some would have had a better chance, some would have had a worse chance, but it would have been 'Zero Sum' overall.

Don't get me wrong. I'm not saying that optimism is always a bad thing. It can boost our self-confidence, which can propel us on to success. Whereas pessimism, on the other hand, can lead to depression.

But, unfortunately, optimism can also encourage us to act irrationally; to pursue unrealistic goals or continue on in jobs and relationships which make us miserable. We delude ourselves into believing that sunny days are just around the corner.

Society encourages this. We're told; *'You can get it if you really want it. You just have to try, try, try!'* And we believe it. We work our arses off. We suffer, in the wildly optimistic hope that we'll be rewarded with a better job, a better salary and a better life, at some mythical point in the future.

In this sense, optimism can be a disease. And I think it's a disease which we all suffer from. This optimism-epidemic, this blind-faith pandemic, dulls our rational capabilities and encourages us to accept our unhappy lives.

At least that's what I did.

Even though I didn't want to do it, I ploughed on through my degree because I was optimistic that it'd lead to a good job. Even though it seldom made a difference, I obeyed my bosses, teachers and parents, in the optimistic hope that it'd make them happy. Even though my previous relationships had never worked out, I was still optimistic that things would go well with Lorraine. And even though I wasn't promoted whilst working as a fundraiser, I was still optimistic that I'd be promoted whilst working as a junior chef. I was optimistic that I'd become a head chef, with a permanent contract and a living wage.

Albert Einstein once said that 'insanity' was *'Doing the same thing over and over again, expecting to achieve different results'*. He was a clever chap, that Einstein fella. And, according to him, I must have been insane. Because I kept on working hard, and I kept on expecting to be rewarded, even though my hard work had never been rewarded before. I didn't have any evidence to suggest that I'd be rewarded. It wasn't a rational belief. It all came down to optimism. Blind, debilitating optimism.

I turned up early and stayed late. I helped to train new members of staff. Whenever there was a quiet spell, I found something productive to do; cleaning, prepping or stock-taking. I worked through my breaks. And

I followed all the rules.

I never complained.

I never complained when I had to do split-shifts. I never complained when I had to work until two o'clock in the morning. I never complained when I had to start again at eight o'clock the next morning, having only slept for three hours.

Yet the only pay-rise I received was tiny. And that wasn't a result of my hard work; it was a pay-rise that everyone got after six months of employment. I never got promoted. I never became a head chef.

After a year had passed, Lorraine dumped me. She said that she *'really liked me'*. But we were just *'too incompatible to be together'*.

I didn't even feel that bad. Not like when Georgie dumped me. My skin didn't stretch taut. I didn't cry into my pillow. I just accepted it. I just felt apathetic.

And then, after another four months had passed, I was turfed out of the apartment that Lorraine and I had shared. My landlord wanted to give it to his son. So I had to pack my bags and move into a claustrophobic studio flat.

Dear reader, as I regale you with this sorry series of events, I can't help but think of a Lao Tzu saying; *'If you don't change direction, you may end up where you're heading'*.

Well, I didn't like *'where I was heading'*; a life full of long hours and low pay, uncomfortable working conditions and little free time. I realised that I needed to *'change direction'*. That I needed to find a new job.

I was still optimistic. I was still hopeful that I could land a better job, with better working conditions. I was still hopeful that job would enable me to make more of a contribution to society and earn more money for myself. I still daydreamed about buying my own flat.

So I applied for other jobs. I applied for the sort of jobs I believed someone with my degree should be doing. And I was optimistic about getting those jobs, because I had work experience as well as qualifications.

I did get another job, but it was hardly the job I'd been hoping for.

Dear reader, I became an energy salesman!

I stood in a shopping centre, next to a pop-up stand, and I cajoled passers-by into changing their electricity supplier. I don't think I ever saw myself doing that job for long, but it did pay slightly more than my previous role, so I still considered it to be a step in the right direction.

I trod the tiles of that shopping centre every day. I accosted thousands of bystanders. And I thrust flyers into the preoccupied hands of hurried folk.

The omnipresent white light, which reflected off of every surface, created an eternal midday. Yet I lived in a permanent dusk. It was always dark by the time I stepped outside. I became a stranger to the sun. And I went for a whole year without seeing a single rainbow. Even if I had seen a rainbow, I'd have probably ignored it.

I ploughed on.

I signed people up for 'Fixed Plans', 'Indexed Plans' and 'Prepaid Plans'. I set up 'Direct Debits', 'Standing Orders' and 'Customer Accounts'. I completed the paperwork, kept my stall in order, and grinned like a Cheshire cat.

On and on it went; day after day after day.

NINETEEN

My job was a bit of a drag. Pretty much every day was the same. But, every once in a while, something would happen which shook me out of my monotony-induced trance.

One day, for example, I saw a young lady walk by. She had a pregnant glow which shone right through her two-piece suit. The fine diamonds in her ears sparkled. And the red paint on her lips glistened.

I caught her eye.

And then my heart stopped. My stomach dropped. My face turned ice-cold.

I realized who it was.

It was Sleepy Sampson! Remember her? She was the girl who hummed during quiet time. The one who'd pinned me to the floor, after I'd scolded her, and said; *'You're not the boy we all used to love. You're not the boy I used to love!'*

Well, dear reader, there she was; all slinky lines and luscious bulges. Delicate warmth radiated from her cherry blossom cheeks. A coltish giggle danced on her chary tongue.

"Hey!" I called.

Sleepy Sampson ignored me.

That was normal; being ignored was part of the job. No-one wanted to be accosted by the pesky salesman. Most people pretended that I didn't even exist.

"Sleepy!" I called out again. "Hey! Sleepy! Sleepy Sampson!"

And then she flinched. As if a ghost had passed through her, she almost shivered and she almost shook. Without moving her head, she turned one eye towards me.

My face reflected in her cornea.

She saw me. Her head shot round, dragging her body with it. Her face lit up; illuminated by the enlightenment of recognition and the innocence of surprise. White light flickered in her eyes and a pinkish flush swept across her countenance.

"Yew!" she sang.

I blushed.

"Yew! How are you?" she asked.

"I'm good. It's great to see you. It's been so long!"

"Sixteen years!"

"Sixteen years?"

"Sixteen years! I haven't seen you since the last day of primary school. Do you remember it? We took photos on the grass and swore that we'd stay friends forever."

"Yeah, I remember that! We all got given bibles. We wrote messages on the blank pages. And then we signed each other's uniforms."

"If you'd told me back then that we wouldn't meet for another sixteen years, I wouldn't have believed you."

"Me too! Where has the time gone?"

"Time flies."

"It does. Just look at you! You're not so scrawny anymore!"

"And look at you! You're not so sleepy!"

"Oi you, you cheeky bugger! No-one has called me that in years."

"So what do people call you these days?"

"Mrs Smith."

'Mrs Smith' dropped her wrist to reveal the ring which took pride of place on her finger.

"You're married?"

"Sure am!"

"Who's the lucky man?"

"Brian."

"Brian? Brian Smith? Chubby Smith? The boy with more blubber than a killer whale? The beast of the east? The man mountain of the water fountain?"

"Oi! Stop it you little rascal. Brian's not fat anymore. He's a successful banker."

"A banker? Good for him! And what are you doing with yourself?"

"Oh, you know, this and that. I'm a PA to the Chief Executive of a big firm. But I've been spending most of my time doing up our holiday home. It's really been taking it out of me. Sometimes I think home ownership is more stress than it's worth. But, you know, you've to plough on through."

I giggled uncomfortably.

"Look, I need to be getting off," 'Mrs Smith' continued. "The boss is a bit of a slave driver, if you know what I mean. But it'd be great to catch up. Do you fancy grabbing a coffee sometime?"

I nodded.

"Cool! I'll be in touch."

Sleepy Sampson swished her hair as she turned. Her feet glided away. And her form evaporated.

I froze.

I was gobsmacked. I just couldn't fathom what had just happened.

'*How on earth could Sleepy Sampson be such a success?*' I asked myself.

She was the girl who slept through class after class. She hardly paid any attention at school. Her grades were terrible.

She was the girl who didn't react when I wiped my nose on her sleeve. She didn't care. She was indifferent to the world.

She was the girl who hummed during quiet time. She didn't follow the rules. She didn't try to please her superiors. She didn't try to please anyone at all. She wasn't selfless like me. She was selfish to the core.

Yet she was beautiful. She was happily married, with a good job and a holiday home. A holiday home! I couldn't even afford to buy a studio flat, and she owned a holiday home!

It just didn't seem fair. It didn't seem right.

For the first time in years, my apathy gave way.

I was fuming. My face was on fire!

Like a fire-breathing dragon, steamy air poured out of my flared nostrils. My skin became reptilian. My eyes bulged.

People gave me a wide berth.

I stewed in the sloppy goulash of my fury. Lumps of my indignation, and morsels of my irritation, sloshed about in a soup of my despair.

'How could she try so little and get so much, when I try so much and get so little?' I asked myself. *'Why should I subject myself to society's demands, when someone like Sleepy Sampson can glide through life whilst staying true to herself? Why bother? Why?'*

That same dull, gentle, element of doubt, which had pulsated beneath the surface of my conscious mind when I was asked to perform a religious ceremony, and when I was taken into a strip club, began to thud once again. And it wasn't just a dull thudding. It was a real tub-thumping, heart-pumping sort of thudding. It was as if a new reality was being born; breaking the waters of my mind, dilating the shackles I'd placed upon my thoughts, and releasing my inner-child back into the world.

I had to grab hold of my stall in order to remain upright. My legs had turned to jelly. My head felt light and my stomach felt queasy.

I didn't tidy my stall that evening. I didn't complete the daily sales report. I just stumbled out into the evening hue and melted into the fuzzy blur of my twisted reality.

The air tasted of sulphur.

TWENTY

Lao Tzu once said; '*A leader is best when people barely know he exists. When his work is done, and his goals have been achieved, they will say 'We did it ourselves'.*'

My boss, Dave, was nothing like that. I definitely knew he '*existed*'. He never let me say '*I did it myself*'.

Rather than suggest an objective and leave me to achieve it, he'd demand that I do things his way. That lanky, rangy man would tower over me, leaving me in no doubt that he expected me to do as he said.

Rather than praise my major achievements, he'd lambast me for my minor mistakes. He spoke like a lion. Sometimes he'd roar. But, more often than not, he'd simply purr with self-assurance.

And rather than say, '*How do you think we should do this?*', he'd say, '*Do it like this!*'

Psychologists, such as John Sensenig and Jack Brehm, will tell you that such behaviour is a recipe for disaster.

Those men conducted an experiment in which volunteers had to react to a list of statements using a scale, with 'Strongly Agree' at one end, 'Strongly Disagree' at the other, and twenty-nine points in-between.

The volunteers were then told that they were going to write essays supporting or opposing five of those statements. The first, '*Federal aid to church-run schools should be discontinued*', hadn't elicited any passionate responses. The other four statements had.

The volunteers were split into pairs.

Volunteers in the 'Low Threat Group' were told that one member of their pair would choose whether to argue for or against the first statement, and that both members would then have to take that side. The person making the decision was allowed to ask their partner for their opinion. But when it came to the other four essays, both people were told that they could take whatever side they liked.

Volunteers in the 'High Threat Group', however, were told that one member of their pair would choose sides for all five essays.

The experiment was rigged. None of the volunteers got to choose sides. They were all put in isolated rooms. Then they were given a note, which they were told came from their partners, but which had in fact been written by a researcher. That note always asked them to take the side they'd originally taken in the survey, so there was no conflict.

A 'Control Group' within the Low Threat Group were given notes which said, *'I'd prefer to agree/disagree with this, if it's okay with you'*. Those notes involved the volunteers in the process.

The rest of the volunteers were given notes which said, *'I've decided we will both agree/disagree with this'*. Those notes coerced the recipient.

Then, whilst writing their essays, the volunteers were asked to react to the statement again, using the original thirty-one point scale.

Here's what happened:

Volunteers in the Control Group expressed a stronger belief, for or against the statement, than they had done in the original survey. They reacted positively because they'd been involved in the process.

But the rest of the Low Threat Group expressed a weaker belief. They felt threatened. They didn't like being told what to write, even though they actually agreed with the opinion which was being forced upon them.

And the people in the High Threat Group expressed an even weaker belief. On average, they shifted their responses by 4.17 places on the scale, away from the view being imposed on them, even though they originally agreed with that point of view. They felt threatened by the idea of being told what to write about another four (much more emotional) issues.

This shows that when a person's freedom is threatened, they will take steps to restore those freedoms which are under threat. They will move their own opinions on an issue away from the opinions which are being forced upon them, even if they originally supported those opinions.

Well, dear reader, that's exactly what happened to me!

You see, my conversation with Sleepy Sampson had encouraged me to assess my situation. It had encouraged me to assess the way my boss was treating me.

My boss told me how I should hold myself, how I should smile and how I should approach people. He wrote my pitch. And he insisted that I use scripted answers to manage objections.

Most of the time I agreed with my boss's points of view. I learned a lot from that rambunctious young man. But it was the very fact that he was telling what to do that really grated. I felt that he was threatening my freedom.

And so, in response to that threat, I started to move my own beliefs away from the beliefs which were being forced onto me.

It's like Lao Tzu says; *'The more laws and order are made prominent, the more thieves and robbers there will be'*.

Well, my boss was big on *'order'*. It didn't make me a *'thief'* or a *'robber'*, but it did make me want to rebel.

For the first time since the egot died, I actually started to question authority! I questioned everything Dave told me to do:

'Why should I stand as he tells me to stand?'

'Why should I smile when he tells me to smile?'

'Why should I use his script?''

That subtle element of doubt, that dull thudding which resurfaced when I spoke to Sleepy Sampson, transformed into a new consciousness. It dominated my thoughts. It made me question everything:

'Why should I obey my teachers, parents and bosses?'

'Why should I conform to societal norms?'

'Why should I bend to peer pressure?'

'Why should I follow the law?'

'Why should I deny my true self?'

My mind was a tangle of distinct but interconnected anxieties. A real fireball of anger. A real punching-bag of angst.

I'd done everything everyone had ever wanted of me. I'd followed all their rules. I'd respected authority. I'd gone to university. I'd worked hard, worked well and worked long hours. Yet I hadn't been rewarded. I hadn't been promoted. I wasn't receiving a decent wage. And I couldn't afford to buy myself a flat.

Something had to give. I mean, other people were earning good wages. Other people could afford to buy their homes. Even Sleepy Sampson was getting on in life. She owned two homes! And she'd never worked as hard as I had. The only thing she was good at was sleeping!

My mind was full of thoughts like these.

As if a cork had been removed from my subconscious, twenty years of bottled-up frustrations gushed out into my conscious mind.

I suppose you could compare my mental state to an elastic band.

An elastic band can be stretched to many times its natural length. It can be twisted out of all recognition. But there's only so far you can stretch an elastic band before it'll snap back into place.

Well, dear reader, I'd reached that point. Snapping point! I was snapping back into my natural form.

The egot was dead. But I didn't need it. I was thinking for myself, without its help. Its little voice had become a bellowing battle cry. And it was *my* battle cry. It was my little voice. It was mine, all mine!

Everything was clear. It was clear that I'd been living in a cage. It was clear that freedom was mine to take. It was clear what I had to do. I was my own clarity. Everything was clear.

Dave swaggered towards me. He towered above me. His whiskers twitched and his mane swished.

Without stopping to say 'hello', he immediately began to dictate terms:

"You need to stop using the word 'we'," he said. "You need to use the words 'us' and 'our' instead."

But I was oblivious to that man. I was oblivious to the world.

I remember a sense of otherworldliness, as if I'd stepped outside of the physical realm. My legs lifted my torso, my frame stood tall, and my spirit stood still. My body melted away from my control.

I watched on as my body broke free. As it leapt up onto the stall. As it pounded its breast like a valiant ape. And as it puffed its chest like a swashbuckling superhero.

The faint sound of Beethoven's Ninth Symphony started to fill my ears. Delicate violin strings provided a melodic backdrop for the ballet which was unravelling on stage.

My boss opened his jaw, as if to roar.

My body performed a pirouette.

Flyers rose up beneath my feet and span around my shins like froth on a choppy ocean.

I felt an all-encompassing surge of bliss.

One leg rose up in front of my body, forming a sharp arrow which pointed out towards the soulless expanse of that hall. I held that position perfectly still, whilst lifting my chin with a pompous sort of grace. Then I leapt like a spring deer, in slow motion, with one leg pointing forward and the other one darting back.

Beethoven's Ninth sounded glorious as it purred through the gears. Violas joined violins and cellos joined those violas. Double basses began to hum and flutes began to whistle.

I landed with my feet together; an angel of the air, a demon of the sea.

My mind floated atop an infinite ocean.

My arms swept through the infinite air. They knocked over the board behind my stall. They overturned my table. They sent paperwork up into the bright white light.

I could see my monkey soul. I could hear the monkey calls which were emanating from my open mouth. I could hear Beethoven's Ninth reach its first crescendo, as the brass section began its battle cry. Flutes became one with clarinets. Bassoons boomed. Trumpets and horns squealed with uncontrollable delight.

I howled like a donkey at the moment of sexual climax.

My lungs filled with pure spirit.

I tore off my shirt and faced my boss. My hairy chest bulged like a gorilla's breastplate. My shoulders protruded from my upper back. And my temples were as erect as horns.

I encircled that man, toying with him like a cat might toy with a mouse. And I stampeded around him like a herd of untamed wildebeests; leaving the rubble of my stall, some twisted shoppers and some miscellaneous debris in my wake.

Beethoven's Ninth called out for redemption, glory and release. It was an impassioned cry. It was a fury-filled yell.

"Yew! Yew! Yew!" my boss was yelling.

But I didn't care.

"Fuck you!" I cheered. "Fuck you Dave!

"Fuck you! Fuck you! And fuck your fucking job!"

I floated on the winds of time. I danced above the starry earth. And I flew through the eternal ether.

My body left that shopping centre behind it.

My soul said 'good riddance' to that bullshit job.

TWENTY ONE

I was jobless and a few months away from being penniless. But I didn't care.

I'd re-found myself. I'd liberated myself. I'd experienced the euphoric bliss of rebellion. And it'd ignited a burning hunger within me.

I wanted more!

I wanted more out of body experiences. More transcendence. More elation.

I wanted Beethoven's Ninth to whisper sweet nothings in my ear.

I wanted to satisfy my animal urges.

And so I didn't just rebel reactively. No.

Dear reader, for the first time in my life I proactively searched for opportunities to rebel. To kick-out against the system. To assert myself.

I went to an anti-capitalist rally.

It was a carnival, full of all the assorted misfits and mavericks you might expect to find in a 1960s hippy commune. Bare-chested men wore mesmeric waistcoats. Dreadlocked ladies wore Indian skirts. Grey-haired sages mingled with babes-in-arms. And middle-aged eccentrics mixed with ageless revolutionaries.

Those activists planted marijuana plants in Parliament Square. It was genius! They put a grass Mohican atop a statue of an old dictator. And they scrawled graffiti over a monument which glorified war.

My heart pounded. My veins throbbed.

Those were my people! Like-minded spirits! Soul siblings!

I finally felt at home.

I was swept up in a wave of those people's energy, carried down the street, and delivered into the crowd which had gathered around a multinational junk-food restaurant.

Protestors were smashing that place apart. Windows were shattered and tables were overturned. Kitchen appliances lay crying on their sides. The beaten remains of that capitalist outpost were bleeding on the floor.

My little voice, that little voice inside my head which had lain dormant for years, which had reappeared when I rebelled against my boss, and which had been speaking to me ever since, told me to join in. It was a quiet voice, much like the egot's quiet voice. It was calm. Subtle. Quirky. And it told me to join in. It told me to contribute. It told me to help that rebel army to create a better world.

And I listened. Dear reader, I listened to my little voice! Not to the egot. Not to the calls of others. But to <u>my</u> little voice. That manifestation of the real me.

I pushed through the crowd. I squeezed between veteran activists with brightly coloured hair. And I slunk between confused tourists who'd been caught up in the melee. In and out. In and out. Until I eventually reached the front.

By the time I arrived the activists had moved onto the money exchange next-door. Its door had been removed. Protestors were tearing that place to smithereens.

I picked up a chair, lifted it high above my head, and smashed it into the window. It hurt. The vibrations from the strengthened-glass ran up my arm. My shoulder jolted backwards.

The shattered glass wobbled and then returned to its original position. Thousands of shards were still held in place by some sort of synthetic sheet. My half-hearted swing hadn't made a difference.

But I felt great. Not euphoric. Not ecstatic. But great. Really, really great.

I felt that I was *sticking it to the man*. To the man who'd groomed me at school. To the man who'd made me go to university and then abandoned me. To the man who'd led me into a strip club, like a dog on a lead, and expected me to be grateful. And to the man who'd made me speak from a stupid script, day in day out.

I felt that I was sticking it to those men. I felt that I was sticking it to all the men. I felt that I was standing up, not only for myself, but for every other worker who was stuck in a call centre, making monotonous calls, helping some rich person to get even richer. For every other worker who never knew when their next shift would be, when their next paycheque would arrive, or when they'd be able to afford to eat. And for every other worker who'd lost all hope. Who felt helpless and alone.

That selfless urge surged through me.

I took a deep breath and looked up at the money exchange. For me, in that moment, it represented everything wrong with the world. Every dead-end job, hard sale and nasty boss. I felt that I had to take it out.

So I lifted the chair once more, swung it once more, and smashed it into the storefront once more. Nothing changed. The glass remained intact. My shoulder took the full weight of the blow.

I repeated the process a third and final time. But it didn't make a difference. And it seemed to me that it wouldn't make a difference if I continued on.

People were staring. They were making me feel self-conscious, paranoid and insecure. An icy-shiver ran through me. My heart seemed to drop.

My little voice told me that I'd done enough.

And so I disappeared back into the crowd.

Looking back on that day now, I can't help but feel that it was a positive experience. I'd connected with thousands of like-minded souls for the first time in my life. I'd become a part of a bigger whole. And I'd tried to contribute - to do my part. At times, that had made me feel great. It had made me feel real.

But it hadn't made me feel euphoric. I didn't transcend the material realm. Beethoven's Ninth didn't ring in my ears.

And, because of that, a part of me still felt unfulfilled...

TWENTY TWO

I still went to a number of protests in the weeks which followed. I protested for peace, the environment and social justice. I protested against nuclear weapons, tuition fees and the arms trade. And I enjoyed those protests. I really did. But I never got high off them. I never felt like I did when I rampaged around Ms Brown's classroom.

I still took part in those protests because I felt that I was making a difference. I felt that I was contributing to society. Well, I felt that I was contributing more than I ever had done by working.

And I still went on those protests because I'd made friends with a group of activists. I liked spending time with them. And I needed them. My old friends all had careers and long-term partners. Some of them had kids. But I'd ostracised myself from the world they lived in. I was different. An outcast. A misfit. And that had put a strain on our relationships. I did manage to stay friends with Gavin Gillis and a few mates from university, but that was it. I never saw any of my work mates again.

Relations with my family also became strained. They just didn't understand what I was doing with my life. They couldn't accept me.

But I still needed companionship. I still needed friendship. And I think that's why I grew closer to my new activist friends.

There was Swampy who, as you might have guessed from his name, was a stereotypical hippie; all tie-dyed shirts, clumpy hair and tatty sandals. There was Brian, who wasn't at all the sort of person you'd associate with activism; he owned a chip shop and had a young family in a quaint historical village. And then there was Becky. Strong, fiery Becky. She was a feminist. And not the airy-fairy type either.

I loved Becky. I mean, I genuinely loved her.

Lao Tzu says that love is *'The strongest of all passions, for it simultaneously attacks the head, the heart and the senses'*.

Well, that's exactly how I felt when I was with Becky. I felt that I was being *'attacked'* by love. Beaten down by it. Kicked in the balls by it.

Becky made me feel great. Really great.

My apathy had washed away. Walking out on my job had enabled me to re-engage with the full emotional spectrum. It had enabled me to feel great again. And it had enabled me to feel morose again too.

So I was able to fall in love. I was able to give myself to that beautiful young lady.

Like with Georgie, I got butterflies in my stomach whenever I saw Becky. Sometimes she'd say things which would really resonate. Things which gave me goose-pimples. She made me feel gooey inside. She made my innards feel like melted marshmallows.

Yeah, I really liked Becky. I really liked all those activists. They all had hearts of gold.

So I still went on those protests. I went on those protests in order to spend time with those great people.

I went on those protests until one gnarly autumn day, when the trees were all full of rusty leaves and the sky was filled with a hazy rainbow. Ominous shades of blue, indigo and violet, provided a grisly backdrop for our angst-filled chants. And lines of orange, yellow and green, brought forth little flickers of hope; hope that we'd actually be able to make a difference, and improve our broken society.

I ignored that rainbow. I was indifferent to it. For me, it was just a prosaic part of the background.

I was totally focussed on our protest.

Our group of activists walked down the high street and then tried to enter a job centre, to stage a sit-in. But a line of burly policemen, who all had chiselled jaws and sculpted chests, blocked the front door. They stopped us from exercising our legal right to stage a peaceful protest.

Political rap boomed out of a ghetto blaster:

'*Forget what they told you in school. Get educated!*'

"It's Akala," Swampy told me. "It's good, eh?"

"Yeah," I replied. "Conscious lyrics man!"

Swampy tapped his sandal-clad foot in time with the music:

"That guy is a Pied Piper for revolutionary rats."

I smiled.

"His songs are rebel anthems for the disenfranchised youth."

I winked.

Baffled locals pretended not to stare.

And a protestor threw a handful of confetti over the policemen. It was hilarious. That protestor effeminised those gargantuan hulks; showering them with delicate paper petals as if they were blushing brides at a country wedding.

The policemen stood stony-faced. They were clearly uncomfortable. Their embarrassment seemed to be veering towards resentment.

But they didn't move an inch.

So some other activists joined in. They all rained confetti down on those policemen.

I joined them. I threw a handful of confetti up into the air. Then I threw a second.

The policemen's frustration began to build. You could see it in their eyes, which were full of bloodshot anger. And you could see it in their auras, which were red with vicious spite. The rainbow's glow created a bloody haze around them. Red leaves danced between their shiny boots.

But they didn't move an inch.

So I threw a third handful of confetti. Then a fourth.

A policeman snapped. Just like that! It happened in the blink of an eye.

That policeman couldn't hold himself back. His animal instinct burst through his self-restraint. His body shot towards me.

I shot back through the protestors, who formed a protective wall between the policemen and myself. I paused. I was ready to stand my ground and protest my innocence.

"Run!!!" Swampy shouted.

"Run!!!" my little voice whispered.

"Run! Run! Run!"

I ran.

I ran down the high street. I hurdled the swinging leg of an elderly have-a-go-hero. And I swung right into a soulless shopping centre.

White light burned my retinas and a stitch tore through my ribs.

But I kept running.

I kept running despite the pain. I kept running despite the futility of it all. I kept running until a security guard stepped out of a privately owned shop. He blocked my way. He towered over me like a giraffe above an ant. And he ground his teeth like a tormented bull.

There was no way I was getting past.

So I put my hands on my knees and inhaled. The air tasted salty.

A policeman caught me up, handcuffed me and led me away. He paraded me past an audience of nosy shoppers and preening kids. They all seemed to be mocking me. They all seemed to be staring.

I felt sick. Physically sick! My stomach was full of adrenaline. It was a vessel of bitter acid. A balloon of acrid spew. A beaker of filth.

I was taken to a police station and locked inside a cell.

Then, after ten hours had passed, I was released. The duty officer told me that I was going to face charges of *'Assaulting an Officer of the Law'*. And that was that!

Fifteen activists picked me up in a rented minibus. They were like wise old kings; bearing gifts of beer, which was ice-cold, some incense and some liquor. They told me not to worry. That everything would be okay. And they made rude gestures at the cops who'd arrested me.

That cheered me up no end. It felt great to know that I wasn't alone. That there were other people out there just like me.

I loved those people's team spirit. For me, they were like a slug of whiskey on a stormy day. A warm blanket on a chilly night. A hug in a moment of dire loneliness.

They made me feel good. They made me feel great. But that feeling was just a fleeting sensation. It wasn't liberation or enlightenment. It wasn't euphoria. And it wasn't a feeling that'd last…

TWENTY THREE

I had to go to court three times after that.

My first appearance was for a plea-hearing. I pleaded *'Not Guilty'*.

My second appearance was meant to be for the trial itself. But it was postponed because the police hadn't given my lawyers the CCTV footage.

My third appearance was also meant to be for the trial. But the police witnesses didn't even turn up! They'd realised that they didn't have a case. And so all the charges were dropped.

The whole process was a real ball-ache. A real twisted sort of psychological warfare. I stressed something chronic.

However, one positive did come out of it.

In order to get a defence lawyer, I had to claim 'Legal Aid'. In order to claim Legal Aid, I had to prove that I was on a low income. And in order to prove that I was on a low income, I had to sign on for 'Job Seekers' Allowance'. I claimed 'Housing Benefit' whilst I was at it.

I'd never claimed benefits before. I'd always thought that welfare was for scroungers and bums. I'd thought that people should earn their money rather than rely on the state.

Yet, in those circumstances, I didn't have a choice. And, in the end, I did rather well out of it. Receiving that money meant I didn't need to work. It meant that I could focus on my real needs.

But I did stop my activism. Political protest hadn't helped me to reach the euphoric state I'd craved. So I asked myself if it was worth all the effort. And, in the end, I concluded that it wasn't. My little voice told me that those protests weren't making the world a better place. And I knew that they weren't making me happy.

I loved my activist friends, and I wanted to stay in contact with them. That was easier said than done. I did manage to stay in contact with Swampy, but Becky dumped me. We'd lost the one thing which had held us together.

That got me down. But it didn't sway me. I was sure that activism wasn't the answer to my problems. I was convinced that I had to put my days of protest behind me.

I'd had a taste of something better, something purer, and I was determined to experience that again. I was one hundred percent focussed on that goal.

But, no matter how hard I tried, I just couldn't reach the highs I'd once experienced. And that ate me up inside. It made me feel like a failure. It made me feel helpless and meek.

I was miserable. I was depressed.

But let me ask you this; *'What sort of person isn't depressed these days?'*

I think Jiddu Krishnamurti got it right when he said; *'It's no measure of health to be well adjusted to a profoundly sick society'*.

Well, I wasn't *'well adjusted'* to my society. I wasn't *'well adjusted'* at all. But my society was *'profoundly sick'*. It'd lost touch with nature, with humanity, and with itself. <u>It</u> was making me sick.

I was ill. I was unhappy. I was depressed.

I felt that no matter what I did, no matter how hard I tried, I just couldn't find happiness. I'd tried to fit in, but it hadn't gotten me anywhere. It hadn't made my parents, my teachers or my bosses happy. And it certainly hadn't made me happy. I hadn't got the promotions I'd desired. I hadn't been able to buy myself a flat. And I hadn't felt fulfilled. I mean, I'd been denying my true self. How could I have possibly felt fulfilled? How could I have possibly been happy?

So I'd rejected my society, but I'd still not found myself. I'd found some happiness, but not true happiness. Not complete happiness. And, in the meantime, I'd become an outcast. A pariah. Rejected by my community. Estranged from my family. And alienated from my friends.

It was an expensive price to pay. I felt utterly alone. Utterly lost. Utterly confused.

My little voice, that quiet voice inside my head, told me to look elsewhere for the highs I was seeking. And so, after much deliberation, I decided to turn to drugs.

I started off with antidepressants. Pink ones, blue ones, yellow ones. You name it, I took it. I took them all!

I only took a couple a week to start with. Then I began to take those pills every day. I took two a day. Then four. Then six.

Those little nuggets of release really worked their way into my neurotransmitters. They really made themselves at home in there; cleaning up my serotonin and scrubbing my norepinephrine clean away.

I felt a tiny bit of bliss each time I took those antidepressants. My mind became clear and my body became light.

But, alas, that bliss never lasted. And there were side-effects too. I suffered from diarrhoea and constipation; insomnia and drowsiness; headaches and dizziness.

I still felt unfulfilled, cast adrift and alone. I still wanted more. I still longed to fly free. I still longed to hear Beethoven's Ninth ring in my ears.

So I moved on to cocaine. And *boy-oh-boy* was it amazing. It was out of this world.

Yee-haw! Whoopee! Hell yeah!

When I took cocaine, *joie de vie* flowed through my veins. A massive grin covered my face. I left my worries behind and danced on through the night.

But that feeling never lasted either. I needed another hit every hour to maintain the high. And, unfortunately, I simply couldn't afford it.

So I looked in on myself. I questioned myself. I questioned my very existence. I questioned everything:

'Who Am I? What am I? What do I want?'

'What on earth am I doing with my life?'

'Do I really think I can find happiness in this bitter and twisted world?'

'What's the point in even trying?'

'Why don't I end it all?'

Pause. Inhale. Exhale.

Relax.

Breathe.

It's not easy for me to write this, dear reader. But those were my thoughts. And so I feel that I have a duty to include them.

Yes, I was thinking of taking my life. There, I said it! But please don't consider that melodramatic or morose. That's not how I saw it.

I told myself that suicide would be a great thing. A grand thing. A release from this world of suffering. A transcendence to a purer realm, free from the shackles of this base existence.

I'd be taking control of my life. I'd be the master of my fate. I'd be the captain of my destiny.

I'd be doing things on my terms. My terms! Just like when I rampaged around my primary school. And just like when I quit my job.

I didn't consider suicide a cowardly retreat; flying away from my problems. I considered it a brave advance; stepping out into the unknown. It wasn't an admittance of defeat. No. It was a victory. A victory of hope over despair, faith over doubt, and choice over coercion.

And so I researched it. I read everything I could about suicide. About how to hang oneself, how to electrocute oneself, and how to slit one's wrists. I'll spare you the gory details. But, needless to say, I did give those methods some serious consideration.

My thoughts, therefore, diverged along two opposing tangents. On the one hand, I was searching for the ultimate high; the ultimate reason to live. And on the other hand, I was looking for the ultimate low; death.

I was a creature of extremes. Although I suppose you knew that already. I have, after all, already told you about my All or Nothing Personality. I'm a black and white sort of guy.

And yet, paradoxically, these two extremes did converge. I searched for my 'all' and for my 'nothing', my ultimate high and my ultimate low, in the same source: Drugs.

Over the weeks and months which followed, my drug taking really clicked through the gears. I didn't only take cocaine, I took a real bevy of mind-altering substances. A real potpourri of opioids and steroids; pills and powders; uppers, downers and all-rounders.

Each new drug took me a little higher. They took me to the twilight zone. To cloud nine. To seventh heaven. Each new hit took me a little closer to my goals.

Those drugs were either going to bring me nirvana or they were going to kill me. I was sure of it. And I was comfortable with it.

I wanted to die. I longed for death. My little voice called out for it every single day. Every single hour.

I wanted those drugs to raise me up. To carry me on through the golden clouds above. And then, in that instant, I wanted them to end me. To end my misery. To whisk me away from this world of suffering. To bring me eternal peace.

I thought it'd be glorious. I thought it'd be the pinnacle of my earthly existence. My enlightenment. My release. My emancipation.

TWENTY FOUR

I arrived home at my lonesome studio flat and hung my heavy coat on its hook.

It dripped onto the crumbling floor:

'Plip. Plop. Plip. Plop.'

I sat down on my only chair and looked across my measly table.

In front of me were the fruits of days spent trawling the city's many dens of inequity. The disreputable establishments where Dickensian characters wheel and deal with all the entrepreneurialism of our country's finest businessmen. Where you can get hold of anything you want, anything at all, just as long as you're willing to line the hands of those kooky souls with enough silver and gold. And where the sweet smell of sweat, industry and endeavour, mingle with the bitter stench of blood, adrenaline and spunk.

On my tiny, battered table, were all the drugs I'd procured in those subterranean dives. All the coke, glue and amphetamines; mushrooms, painkillers and hash; mescaline, LSD and ketamine.

I was aiming for the ultimate high. And I was prepared to die for it. It was win or bust. All or nothing. I wanted to be released and I didn't care how it happened. It was my time. My moment.

Grey clouds consumed the remaining slivers of blue sky.

I pressed 'play' on my stereo and waited for the faint sound of Beethoven's Ninth Symphony to fill my ears. Delicate violin strings sang a lullaby for my rapture. Hail tapped on my dirty windowpanes.

I started with the coke. I knew where I was with coke - it was an old friend.

A sharp chemical rush surged up my nostrils. Tiny specks of baking-powder flavoured dust cascaded down the back of my throat.

My eyes bulged. My body swayed. My arms were like branches in the wind; at one with nature, at one with time.

Cocaine always gave me that uncontrollable urge to boogie.

I was up on my feet. I was rocking. I was dancing a one-man tango.

Beethoven's Ninth sounded glorious as it purred through the gears. Violas joined violins and cellos joined those violas. Double basses began to hum and flutes began to whistle.

I turned up the volume on my stereo. Then I took some mescaline, which I knocked back with a swig of stale beer.

I'd wanted to take mescaline ever since I read Aldous Huxley's essay, 'The Doors of Perception'. For Huxley, mescaline was '*A toxic shortcut to self-transcendence*'. A door to '*Sacramental visions*' and '*Gratuitous grace*'. A spiritual drug.

Huxley believed that we place straitjackets on our brains; that we block out the spiritual realm in order to focus on the physical world. It's a defence mechanism that helps us to survive here on earth.

But Huxley wanted to break out of that self-imposed straitjacket. He wanted to transcend the physical realm. He wanted to do more than just '*survive*'.

And Huxley wasn't alone. The Huichol people of Mexico also believe that mescaline is a spiritual drug. They use it to heal, build inner strength and discover new prophesies. The Native Americans have been taking mescaline for centuries. Army folk have used it as a truth serum.

So for me, it seemed like the perfect drug. A ladder to the heavens. Spiritual. Enlightening. Transcendental.

I thought I was onto a winner.

I took another couple of lines of coke whilst I waited for the mescaline to kick in. I took some painkillers. And I put Beethoven's Ninth on repeat.

My pulse rate descended.

My heart rate increased.

My little voice whispered:

"Beam me up Scottie. I control your body. We all rock fades, fresh faded in la-di-da-di."

At the gates of a forest I stood.

I heard some mermaids, cooks and field-hands sing a night-song. I approached them. I took mystery as my lover and raised light as her child.

At the gates of Atlantis I stood.

I talked to the Sea Son's resurrected, the solstice of the day, who brought news from the blues of the Caspian.

And I ran to the lights, casting love on the winds. And I ran to the lights of infinity; a pupil of its sight, the wheels were spinning.

Beneath the surface of my purpose, I saw the rumours of ancient man. He was dressed in cloud-faced minstrels in the sky. The moon was my mammy. The storm held my eye.

I presented my feminine side with flowers.

She cut their stems and placed them gently down my throat.

My throat!

It burned! It grated! It stung! It bled!

Beethoven's Ninth reached its first crescendo. The brass section began its battle cry. Flutes became one with clarinets. Bassoons boomed. Trumpets and horns squealed with uncontrollable delight.

The burning faded away.

And in that moment I felt happy. Truly happy. Dreamy. At peace.

A sliver of sunshine crept in between the curtains. It illuminated my face. It illuminated my whole entire world.

I smiled.

I positively beamed!

I inhaled a huge chunk of pure bliss!

I felt that I was on my way to the ultimate high.

And then my heart accelerated; starting off at a dangerous velocity and ending up at a truly supersonic speed. It was irregular, like the cymbals at a jazz concert. It had an inconspicuous rhythm, which rattled away at a thousand beats per minute. And it was electronic. Tight. Manic.

I felt like a belt had been wrapped around my heart at an impossibly tight setting. Bubbling lava surged through my arteries, liquid incandescence gushed through my veins, and burning embers scorched the ends of all my capillaries.

My nerves began to short-circuit.

My clothes bled white sweat.

My skin lost its colour.

Beethoven's Ninth called out for redemption, glory and release. It was an impassioned cry. It was a fury-filled yell.

Every ounce of my being was yelling out for release. Release from pain. Release from perdition. Release from life.

The colours! The colours were everywhere!

I saw red-dusted children dance shadows. I saw white feathers descend, furnished with tidings of my doom. And I saw the firstborn daughter of water-faced darkness. She took the lotus position, with claret blood on her hands.

Poseidon gave me a ball of pink light.

The green river knew my name.

The sun was within me. The water was beneath me. My stomach turned, as if a compass. I prayed to the east and lay there breathless.

Terror paralysed me for a full two hours. Or maybe it was three. Perhaps it was more. Time didn't exist. A clock ticked, but only to mock itself. Its hands didn't move. Its face was blank.

And then I pushed through.

I was so close! So close to that ultimate high. So close to the end.

I grabbed some anonymous pills and shoved them down my throat.

I sniffed some glue.

I sailed off into an infinite sea of nothingness. I was the moon cycles revisited. I was the womb fruit of the sun.

I threw myself overboard, where I overheard the mystery of the undertow. And I understood, that down below, there would be no more chains.

I surrendered breath and name, and I survived as rain.

I was the weatherman.

The clouds said a storm was coming.

A white buffalo was born, already running.

I listened close.

I heard a humming.

TWENTY FIVE

'Beep! Beep! Beep!'

I was falling.

I was floating.

I was a bird. My wings were spread. They were gliding through delicate wisps of smoky cloud. The air was caressing my feathers. The sun was fuelling my flight.

'Beep! Beep! Beep!'

I was driving a car. Only the car wasn't a car, it was an elephant. I was sat inside that elephant, turning a steering-wheel, and looking out through the elephant's mouth.

'Beep! Beep! Beep!'

An anime rabbit lunged at me with a blood-soaked dagger in its paw.

'Beep! Beep! Beep!'

I finally realised that I was in a hospital bed. I was in a coma. Unconscious. Unsure of what was real and what was make-believe.

It was a gut-wrenching blow to my psyche.

I was neither high nor low. I hadn't reached nirvana, nor had I died.

'Beep! Beep! Beep!'

I heard two nurses chatter:

"One the one hand, Steven is a great lover. But on the other hand, Patrick really does love me."

'Beep! Beep! Beep!'

I heard the sound of music.

I heard the hoover.

I heard the nurses speak again:

"It's been decided. We're going to have to amputate his legs."

'Beep! Beep! Beep!'

I was at a party. The guests were all covered in manure. It was vivid. I could actually smell that foul excrement. I was convinced that I was actually there.

'Beep! Beep! Beep!'

I was sold to a sweatshop by a gang of human traffickers. They made me sow branded labels onto generic clothes, twenty-four hours a day.

'Beep! Beep! Beep!'

Stereotype Jesus approached me. He had long brown hair and a long white robe. He was surrounded by a golden hue.

"I can take you to heaven," he said. "But only if you're ready."

I was about to shout out; *'Yes! Yes! Take me! Take me now!'*

But I saw the sadness in my parents' eyes. Sadness was in the air. Small insects were crying. Tiny tears filled eyes.

I paused to think. I thought about my family. About my friends. About my society.

I thought for hours. For days. For weeks.

But my resolution remained firm:

"Take me, Jesus," I said. "Take me away."

Stereotype Jesus looked at me. His countenance was as soft as lamb's wool. I felt that he was smiling at me, even though there wasn't a smile on his face. I felt his love. I felt his warmth.

"Take me away," I repeated.

Stereotype Jesus shook his head.

"I'm sorry," he replied. "It's not your time."

He rose. He kept on rising. He passed through the ceiling. And then he disappeared.

TWENTY SIX

'*Beep! Beep! Beep!*'

They say it's darkest before the dawn. They say nothing worthwhile is easy. They say an awful lot of things, whoever *they* are.

But I understood what they were saying. I knew it'd be hard to turn my life around. But, it's like Lao Tzu says; '*A thousand mile journey begins with a single step*'.

I was ready to make that '*single step*'.

I opened my eyes and awoke from my coma.

Everything was white. Bright white. As sterile as a shopping centre. And as pure as earth's first morn.

An angel in a nurse's uniform stood amidst that whiteness. She wasn't beautiful; she was overweight, with coarse worker's hands and a craggy face. But she was handsome; her skin was as black as the universe and her eyes were as white as the stars. She was alluring. She possessed a certain sort of moreish-ness. A certain sort of gravity, which drew me in towards her.

"Hello 'Sleeping Beauty'," she said.

I blinked the sleep from my eyes.

"Err. Uh," I struggled. "Umm. Hi."

The nurse smiled. It was a chubby smile. A warm smile; fractured by the years and reconstructed by pure emotion.

"Hello my lovely," she said. "I'm Betty."

"Betty?" I asked in a groggy voice.

"Nurse Betty."

"Oh."

"How are you feeling?"

"Hi Nurse Betty."

"Hi Yew."

"You have a nice smile."

"Thank-you."

"I really like your smile."

"Thank-you. How are you feeling?"

"I'm feeling the warmth of your smile."

Nurse Betty tittered.

"And how does your body feel?" she asked.

"Calm. Light. Empty. Non-existent. I don't know. I can't feel it."

"Do you feel any pain?"

"So much pain!"

"Where?"

"In my mind."

Nurse Betty tilted her head. She looked like empathy personified; with elevated eyebrows and sunken cheeks. She made me feel comfortable. I suppose that's why I continued on:

"I wanted nirvana," I explained. "I wanted death. I wanted release, any sort of release. And yet here I am, stuck in the material realm; neither enlightened, nor dead, nor free. And that hurts. It hurts so much."

It was the first time I'd ever told anyone about my feelings. And I did it without even thinking. My little voice remained completely silent. Those words just slipped from my tongue, effortlessly, like water trickling off a declivous leaf.

It felt right. It felt good. It felt like a massive burden had been lifted from my shoulders.

There was love in Nurse Betty's eyes.

Those eyes were whirlpools of translucent empathy. They were vortexes of heart-melting compassion and life-affirming humanity.

"Poor soul," she said.

She placed her hand on my arm.

"Poor soul. We'll have to get you some help."

"You can help," I replied. "I don't need anyone else."

Nurse Betty tensed one cheek.

"I'm not so sure about that," she replied. "I'm just a nurse."

"You're not 'just' anything."

"Well, I'm not trained to help you in that way."

"I don't care about training - that stuff's a bunch of baloney. Just do what comes instinctively. Do the first thing that comes into your mind."

The faint light of recognition trickled across Nurse Betty's face.

"Okay," she said. "Okay, my lovely."

She removed a book from her handbag and then passed it to me.

I took that book, which was entitled *'The Wisdom of Lao Tzu'*, and I began to read.

TWENTY SEVEN

Have you ever seen an adult play with a young child? Those mature, sensible people, often act as if they themselves are children. They make silly sounds, do silly things, and allow their imaginations to run free. It's as if the child is re-teaching them how to play; reminding them of a long lost skill, and helping them to re-connect to their own inner-child.

Well, I experienced a similar process myself, thanks to Nurse Betty. She helped me to re-connect with my inner-child.

It all started with a delicate question:

"Why did you want to die?" she asked me.

I paused.

A sparrow sang a song to its lover.

I looked into Nurse Betty's deep, empathetic eyes. Those eyes which were as white as the stars. And then I answered:

"Because I can't be me," I said. "Society won't allow it."

Nurse Betty bit her lip.

"I just want to be free. Free from social pressures. Free to be myself. My true self. My egot."

"Your egot?"

"Free to be me. Free to listen to my inner voice. Free to be happy."

Nurse Betty nodded.

"You want to play, don't you, my lovely?" she asked.

I shrugged.

My body was eager but my mind was confused. I wasn't sure what Nurse Betty meant by the word 'play'. Playing, for me, meant partaking in a structured activity, like exercising at a gym or dining at a restaurant.

The sort of thing that adults did once they'd finished the serious business of work. I wasn't thinking of the childish concept of play. The urge to partake in that sort of thing had been drilled out of me at school.

"Come," Nurse Betty continued. "Come, come, my lovely."

She helped me out of bed and led me down the corridor. But she didn't just walk down that corridor. Oh no. She skipped! She skipped down that corridor with all the exuberance of a five year old.

And I joined in! Dear reader, I actually skipped down that hall! My little voice said, '*What the hell!*' And I skipped for the first time since I was a child. I swung my legs forward and bounced through the air with all the gaiety of youth.

We skipped together, holding hands, as if we were in a school playground.

We skipped past busy doctors, sickly patients and baffled visitors.

We giggled with glee when the sliding doors opened, as if by magic. And we ran out onto the grass, where we removed our shoes and socks.

That feeling of grass underfoot! That unadulterated magic! That holy elixir!

My toes were massaged by those fluffy green tufts. My soles kissed that soft green carpet. My heels sunk into that luxuriant rug.

Mother Nature tickled my naked feet. The living earth stroked my tired flesh. The crumbs of the centuries absorbed my flaky skin.

It started to rain.

We started to dance.

We held hands and swung around in a circle, whilst the tears of heavenly cherubs caressed our mortal skin.

That crystalline elixir took me away to another place. It was refreshing. Exhilarating. Real.

My heart pumped.

Colour returned to my cheeks.

My little voice cheered with joy.

And the rain gave way to an enchanted rainbow.

I gawked at it. I stared at that thing with open-mouthed and wide-eyed amazement. Childlike amazement. Blissful awe.

The violet was so vivid! The indigo was so indulgent! The red was so real!

As if I was seeing a rainbow for the very first time, the sight of it filled me with wonder. It just seemed so magical to me. So mysterious.

You may recall that I'd felt that way once before. Just before my sword fight with Chubby Smith, I'd gazed out at a rainbow and felt those same emotions. I'd wanted to chase that rainbow too.

But I hadn't felt that way for years. I'd considered rainbows prosaic, a scientific phenomenon; easily ignored and easily forgotten. On the day I was arrested, for example, I was totally oblivious to the rainbow which hung above me. To me, back then, it just wasn't worth considering.

That all changed.

I rediscovered my sense of wonder.

My glutinous eyes feasted on that rainbow's beauty. I ate up those colours, drank down those hazy hues, and devoured that brilliant glow.

Energy returned to my being.

Health returned to my skin.

Nurse Betty took me by my hand. Her coarse skin caressed my palm.

"A family of elves live over there," she said.

I was about to laugh. Indeed, a titter of spontaneous laughter did flirt with my tongue. But it didn't make it any further. My newfound sense of wonder overpowered it, destroyed it and expelled it.

In that moment, I could believe. I'd removed the straightjacket from my mind. And I was ready to see the world in a whole new light. I was ready to break free from the constraints of reason and give myself to the world of infinite possibilities.

"They live in giant caverns beneath the roots of those trees," Nurse Betty continued. "They wear red uniforms and pointy hats. And they cook elaborate banquets using whatever nuts and berries they can gather."

"What sort of dishes do they make?"

"Oh, everything, my lovely! Everything! Cranberry gazpacho. Acorn couscous. Stinging-nettle pie. They make the sort of scrummy dishes that we humans would never even dream of."

"Wow! That sounds great!"

"Sure is!"

"We should ask them for a recipe."

"Ok. Let's do it!"

Nurse Betty led me through a copse of lanky trees. Dark firs stretched their gnarled arms above us. Tangled roots pinched our heels. Leaves crawled up our legs.

"We need to call the elves," Nurse Betty told me. Her craggy face, which had been weathered by the years, was awash with childlike innocence. "We need to call out to them like this:

"'Elfie! Elfie! Where are you Elfie?'"

Nurse Betty looked at me. That chubby smile of hers filled her face. She chuckled and then continued:

"Now you give it a go, my lovely."

I nodded. And, like an adult following a child's lead, I completely lost my inhibitions.

I called out to those elves! I sang to them. I searched for them in the undergrowth. And, when I saw something dart beneath the foliage, I called out *'Elf! Elf! Elf!'*

I was convinced that it was an elf. There was no evidence to support my claim, but I believed. I believed!

We celebrated. We clapped. We kept on clapping. It felt great just to clap.

We hugged. Electricity passed between us. That human contact felt like a huge chunk of bliss.

And we laughed. We laughed out loud. We positively guffawed. Belly-laugh followed belly-laugh. Thunderous guffaws knocked us over. And hearty convulsions forced us to roll around.

It felt amazing.

We laughed and then we laughed some more. We laughed for the sake of laughing. We smiled for the sake of smiling. And we howled for the sake of howling:

'Ah-woo! Ah-woo! Ah-woo!'

A wolf howled back.

A bird sang along.

A rabbit danced.

A tree swayed.

A rainbow smiled.

TWENTY EIGHT

Nurse Betty took me out to play, to frolic in the natural environment, every single morning and every single afternoon. We talked about Father Christmas, the Tooth Fairy, and the gnomes which come alive at night. We sang into the wind. And we danced beneath the rain.

That wonderful lady really helped me to re-connect with my inner-child.

But my inner-child was still just a child. I still needed to nurture it. I still needed to help it to grow into a fully-fledged inner-adult.

I just didn't know how to do that.

Then I listened to a song by Akala called 'Get Educated'. (The song which was playing when I got arrested). You may recall the lyrics I put at the beginning of this book.

Anyway, there was this line which got me thinking:

'Forget what they told you in school. Get educated!'

I'd listened to that song hundreds of times, but those words had never registered. Not until that moment.

In that moment it all seemed clear. It all made sense. I realised that my resentment of school wasn't born out of the education I'd received there. I appreciated that I'd been taught to read and write, add and subtract. No, my resentment was born from my indoctrination. I'd rebelled against that, of course I'd rebelled against that, but I'd never rebelled against education itself.

'Beep! Bop! Beep!'

'I ain't saying play by the rules. Get educated!'

With that one line Akala helped me to realise that education could be rebellious. Education could be the purest form of rebellion. It could be unadulterated insurrection!

And, because of that, it could be liberating:

'*Beep! Bop! Beep!*'

'*Break the chains of their enslavement. Get educated!*'

I realised that I was going to have to get educated. Really educated. I was going to have to educate myself.

So I asked Nurse Betty to get me some books from the library. And, when those books arrived, I immersed myself in their sweet, musty pages. I read about all the psychological concepts which I've introduced to you already.

I read about Nature Deficit Disorder. And I realised that I wasn't alone. That it was natural to feel trapped whilst being made to sit inside a stuffy classroom or a soulless workplace. That children and workers, all across the globe, also felt the same way. That they'd have preferred to have been outside in the natural environment too.

I read about Stanley Milgram's experiment, which helped me to understand my subservience to authority.

I read about Solomon Asch's work, which helped me to understand how peer pressure had swayed me.

And I read about the Optimism Bias, which helped me to understand why I kept on going, even when it was irrational to do so.

But it was discovering Operant Conditioning that affected me the most. It was a real eye-opener. It helped me to understand how my headmaster, teachers and parents, had all conspired to mould me. How their punishments and rewards had made me deny my true self, kill the egot, and lock up my inner-child.

That, it seemed to me, was the root of all my problems

And so I concluded that I was going to have to start from there. I was going to have to undo the damaging effects of my Operant Conditioning. I was going to have to resurrect the egot.

But that, dear reader, was easier said than done. Yes, I'd rediscovered some of my childlike capacities for innocence, wonder, awe, joy, sensitivity and playfulness. But I hadn't re-written history. The truth was that the egot had been denied, neglected, disparaged, abandoned and rejected for many, many years. It had been buried beneath the earth of social pressure. Its body had turned to dust.

I tried to will it back into existence. Honestly, I did! I clamped my eyes together, scrunched my lips up tight, and focussed all my energy onto my brain. I focussed on a mental image of the egot. I called out to the egot. I even prayed for the egot to return. Yeah, that's right. Me, Yew Shodkin, who's never willingly prayed for anything in his life, actually prayed for the egot!

But, alas, it didn't make a difference. The egot was gone and it wasn't coming back. I was going to have to move on without it.

Well, having come to that rather sorry conclusion, I returned to Nurse Betty's Lao Tzu book. And, buried within its well-thumbed pages, I found inspiration. I found hope. I found direction.

Lao Tzu's words really spoke to me. They vibrated on my natural wavelength.

Like this line, for example; '*By letting go it all gets done. The world is won by those who let go. When you try and try, the world is beyond winning*'.

Truer words have never been spoken!

I realised that I'd spent my whole life trying. Trying and trying and trying. Trying to be the student my teachers wanted me to be. Trying to be the son my parents desired. Trying to be the employee my bosses required. Trying to succeed, trying to be the best, trying to earn rewards. Trying to earn a promotion, receive a raise and buy my own home.

It hadn't made a difference. I'd *'tried and tried'* but *'the world was beyond winning'*.

That myth our society is built on, that *'You can get it all as long as you try'*, seemed utterly absurd to me. At best it was a delusion and at worst it was a deliberate sham to keep us all working for the man.

For me, Lao Tzu had got it right. I realised that. I realised that I needed to *'let go'*. Or, as Lao Tzu put it, I needed to *'Manifest plainness, embrace simplicity, reduce selfishness and have few desires'*. Because *'He who knows that enough is enough, will always have enough'*. He will *'Win the world'*.

TWENTY NINE

"Come on then, my lovely," Nurse Betty said. The glow from a street light reflected off her pitch-black skin. The early morning breeze caressed the crumples on her craggy face.

Nurse Betty put my solitary bag, which contained all my life's possessions, into the creaky boot of her rusty old banger. She put her key in the ignition, forced it to turn, and fell back into her dust-filled seat.

That rust-bucket roared into life. It shook from left to right. It vibrated from front to back. And then it jolted forwards.

We crawled through the city's labyrinthine streets; passing grey buildings, grey skies and grey people. And although we had to stop and wait for an endless series of traffic-lights, it felt like we were making real progress. It felt like we were breaking free from the city's robotic grip.

We finally made it. We finally reached a land of unadulterated greenery. A land that you might call the 'Countryside' or the 'Wilderness', but which I prefer to call the 'Natural Habitat'.

We snaked along quaint lanes which were enclosed by antique stone walls. We slipped past grassy fields and trees which were older than time. We slid down muddy tracks which were as sticky as a hot fudge sundae. And we slithered through aqueous brooks.

The air tasted of freedom. The grass smelled of life itself. The birds sang of love.

Nurse Betty sang along with those birds. And so did I! We sang as loudly as we could. Succulent air filled our lungs and sweet rhythm filled our souls. It made me feel free. It made me feel fulfilled.

Dear reader, I really must take this opportunity to mention how grateful I was to Nurse Betty for helping me that day. She didn't have to. She wasn't on the clock. But she helped me nonetheless.

God I loved that woman! I wasn't *in love* with her. I didn't lust for her body. I didn't harbour any romantic feelings for her at all. But I did feel a pure, unselfish sort of love for Nurse Betty. A benevolent sort of love. The sort of love that the Ancient Greeks called 'agape'.

Anyway, Nurse Betty turned off the road and zigzagged through an aromatic copse of dancing trees.

We arrived in a clearing; a glade which was as fresh as a dewy dawn. It was lush. It was inviting.

I inhaled. And I looked up at my new home.

To you, dear reader, that abandoned shack might've looked like a wreck. A mere pile of rocks. But to me it was heaven. It was dreamy. It had four stone walls, plenty of wood, and an abundance of nature's bounty.

My little voice released a huge sigh of relief.

I finally felt like I belonged.

It's like Lao Tzu says; *'The career of a sage is of two kinds: He's either honoured by all in the world, like a flower waving its head, or else he disappears into the silent forest'.*

Well, I'd found my *'silent forest'*, and I was *'disappearing'* into it.

I've been here ever since.

THIRTY

Nurse Betty said '*Goodbye*' and I got to work.

I fixed the roof, using the wood which was propped up against an outside wall, and I made a small stove using the stony rubble which was scattered all around. That hut became a home. It became more than a home. For me, it was a palace, a refuge and a sanctuary.

The rain dripped in through places I hadn't even realised existed. The wind whistled. It twisted and it whirled. But I didn't care. I drank that rain down with gusto. And I sucked in that sweet, saccharine air.

I took it all in and smiled.

What wonder! What beauty! What grace!

I finally felt like I belonged. Like I'd found my natural state.

My whole life began to ebb and flow in time with nature's rhythm.

It's like Lao Tzu says; '*Nature does not hurry, yet everything is accomplished*'.

Well, I didn't '*hurry*'. I made little improvements to my shack each day. I did a little bit here and a little bit there. And, in time, '*everything was accomplished*'.

I constructed a table and some chairs using scavenged wood. I built gutters to collect rainwater. I dug a natural toilet. And I made a small wind-turbine which powered my lamp.

Nurse Betty brought me a mattress and some seeds.

I put the finishing touches to my home and then set to work on the glade, where I planted all the seeds I thought might flourish.

I grew luscious greens, crunchy vegetables and succulent tomatoes; vibrant berries, eager fruit trees and hearty pulses.

I taught myself how to survive. How to turn wood into fire, wheat into flour, and plants into potions. How to forage; how to spot edible berries and mushrooms. How to dry nuts, roast coffee and process rice. How to smoke, dehydrate, salt and pickle fresh food. And how to perform spiritual exercises like meditation and yoga.

My whole life was natural. My whole life was entwined with nature herself.

Nature fed me. Nature freed me. And nature kept me sane.

Please do allow me to explain...

Do you remember when I said I felt trapped at school, just before I had a sword fight with Chubby Smith? Here's what I wrote:

'I was stuck inside and the stifling nature of school was getting to me. I'm a bird, you see; I need to fly free. I need space and freedom... But I was being forced to sit behind a desk; held captive by four insensitive walls and enslaved by my teacher's omnipotent authority... I just didn't feel natural. I didn't feel right.'

Well, that was a recurring feeling which stuck with me, like a leech on a bloody vein, all the way through my youth. It was a nagging feeling. An omnipresent thudding that refused to leave me alone.

But, dear reader, that feeling did leave me alone when I went to live in the forest.

My glade allowed me to *'fly free'*. It gave me *'space and freedom'*. It released me from the *'four insensitive walls'* of my school and the *'omnipotent authority'* of my superiors.

The trees which surrounded me weren't walls. They were porous. The spaces between them were doors into a constantly changing wonderland. A wonderland that amazed me every day.

And I didn't have a boss.

But it'd be wrong to say that I became my own boss, my own master. I didn't boss myself. I didn't master myself. I didn't tell myself what to do.

I simply merged into nature.

I rose with the sun. I glided on the breeze. I inhaled time. And I exhaled space.

I embraced the silence, which was only ever interrupted by an alarm clock I couldn't seem to locate:

'Beep! Beep! Beep!'

The egot never returned. And I was glad of that. I didn't need it. I didn't need *me*. I lost my sense of self; that sense of identity, of individuality, which I'd craved so much as a youngster.

My little voice went quiet.

I no longer saw myself as an individual; a distinct entity set apart from the world. I saw myself as a part of a much greater whole. A drop in an ocean, inseparable from the ocean itself. A star in an infinite galaxy. United. Indivisible. One.

I was nature and nature was me.

I was a bird, an animal and an insect.

I was a dancing tree.

I was a tangled bush.

I was a starry, starry sky.

I was an infinite dome of pure azure.

But, dear reader, I wasn't alone. No.

Nurse Betty came to visit me every few months. Occasionally, she brought me things she thought I might need. She never asked for anything in return. She was benevolent to the core.

On one occasion, she brought me a dog, 'Cloudy'; a soppy old Labrador who'd been abused by her previous owner. Cloudy became my best friend. I cared for her as if she were my own child. She became a great outlet for my selfless urges. And, like me, she was reinvigorated by our natural surrounds.

After a few months had passed we were joined by a ginger cat. I named her 'Betty'. I have no idea where Betty came from. She just turned up and decided to adopt us. She was welcome - we appreciated her company. We still do. She's a strange cat. She's happy to survive on a diet of vegetables. And she spends hours in the rain without even flinching. She looks like she's meditating. But then I suppose that most cats are strange, when you come to think about it. I reckon they have split-personalities. They're unsure whether to consider themselves hunters or prey; to be brazen and bold, or skittish and scared.

The birds who accompanied us weren't so confused. They sat in the branches and sang to their hearts' content. I joined them. So did Cloudy.

Occasionally we were visited by a hopping hare or a bouncing rabbit. We saw foxes and squirrels, badgers and snakes. We even saw a peacock.

So I had everything I wanted and more. I had food and shelter. I had companions. I had peace.

And, in creating such a life, I believe that I nurtured my inner-child.

Once more, please do allow me to explain...

I started this book by regaling you with a story in which my teacher, Ms Brown, spoke about savages:

'A savage is like an animal', she said. 'He doesn't wear clothes, live in a house, study or work. He follows his base urges; to eat, drink and reproduce... He doesn't have any ambition... He does the least he can to survive. And he spends most of his time sleeping or playing.'

That, you may recall, really appealed to me. This is what I wrote:

'It was as if I'd stumbled across a race of super-humans. To me, the savages sounded like gods. I knew at once that I wanted to be one. I'd never been so sure of anything in my life.'

Having learnt about the savages, I listened to the egot for the first time. I went on a rampage, believing that I myself was a savage.

Of course, I wasn't really a savage. But what was true then, was also true when I moved to the forest. I wanted to eat and drink and sleep. I wanted to play. But I didn't want to work. I didn't want to be imprisoned by the shackles of futile ambition.

For years I'd forgotten about those real needs. For years I'd chased the false goals which had been imposed on me by others.

I'd grafted away in jobs I'd never really wanted, without realising how counterproductive that was. It's like Lao Tzu says; *'Fill your bowl to the brim and it will spill. Keep sharpening your knife and it will blunt'*.

I'd sought promotions, without realising that a management position wouldn't ever fulfil me. It's like Lao Tzu says; *'He who controls others may be powerful, but he who masters himself is mightier still'*.

And I'd longed for a pay-rise, without realising that money wouldn't make me wealthy. It's like Lao Tzu says; *'He who is contented is rich'*.

Yet there I was, in my glade, living like a savage. Or rather, perhaps I should say that I was living like a 'Natural Human-Being'. (Because 'savage' is such a derogatory word).

I'd nurtured my inner-child. I'd given it everything it had ever wanted; things like freedom, space and nature. And I'd released it from the things it hadn't ever needed; things like work, ambition and greed.

I'd been a caterpillar, but I'd become a butterfly.

I'd been a seed, but I'd become a flower.

My inner-child had grown into my inner-adult. I'd become myself. My true self. I'd become one.

EPILOGUE

It's been seven years since I first moved to the forest, and my time here has given me the opportunity to think. To judge my situation objectively. And, whilst I can't say that I've come to any concrete conclusions, I do have some reflections which I'd like to share with you, dear reader, before we go our separate ways. I hope these shaggy ramblings will provide you with some food for thought...

Looking back on my first few years here it'd be correct to say that I was happy. Happier than I'd ever been before. I felt a real sort of bliss, as I hope will be apparent from the previous chapter.

That bliss was the result of two distinct factors:

The first factor was positive. I'd found a natural rhythm. I was one with nature; both independent and interconnected, whole and part of a greater whole.

The second factor was negative. I'd escaped an overbearing society, full of overpowering pressures and overblown expectations. I felt like a gargantuan weight had been lifted from my fragile shoulders.

Well, it'd still be true to say that I feel at one with nature. I still rise with the sun, live from the earth, and ebb and flow with nature's earthly tides.

But it'd be remiss of me not to mention that the euphoria of my liberation has worn off. It's true that I don't feel a weight on my shoulders anymore. But I don't feel the relief I felt when that weight was first removed. I don't feel emancipated. I don't feel anything much at all.

Perhaps, at this point, I should mention another Lao Tzu proverb. (I only hope that I haven't bored you with my obsession with that man):

'In dwelling, live close to the ground. In thinking, keep to the simple. In conflict, be fair and generous. In governing, don't try to control. In work, do what you enjoy. In family life, be completely present'.

Well, I certainly dwell close to the ground and I certainly keep my life simple. I enjoy my work, if you can call what I do 'work'. I don't have any conflicts and I've never governed. So I tick five of Lao Tzu's six boxes.

But am I completely present in family life? Clearly not! I couldn't be further removed.

My family lives in my childhood neighbourhood. I live here in this forest. There are miles between us, but there might as well be whole galaxies. To me, it feels like we live on completely different planes.

And this begs another question; *'Can anyone be truly happy, indefinitely, whilst living in solitude?'*

Perhaps some strange individuals can. But we humans are social beings. We need companionship. We need love.

I was made to choose between my society and myself. I chose myself. And I don't regret that at all. I just wish that I'd been born into a world where that choice wasn't necessary. I love the little society I've created here. I love spending time with my dog and my cat. I love seeing Nurse Betty on the rare occasions that she visits. But I do still long to live in a good human society; a society that can accept me for who I am.

I love the birdsong that serenades my every hop, skip and jump. But I do still long for the inimitable harmony of human laughter. For the warm, uninhibited sound of another person's glee. For the snug embrace of another, the lively pitter-patter of joyous conversation, and the raucous melody that accompanies a shared meal.

I love the cosy charm of a cold night and the melancholy embrace of a clammy day. I love my connection with nature. But nature can be so unforgiving! I do sometimes crave the comforts of a well-built home. One that doesn't get unbearably hot or cold, wet or claustrophobic. One that has a bath or a shower or a good selection of books.

Sometimes I ask myself, '*Is this what I really want?*'

And I can't answer that question. I don't know. I don't know. I just don't know.

So let's ask another question which I can answer; '*Have I reached enlightenment?*'

The answer to this one is a firm 'no'. I know that for sure. I might never reach enlightenment. I'm not even sure if 'enlightenment' exists. (Although if it does, and if I do make it, I'll be sure to let you know).

A third question; '*Have I had any out of body experiences, where Beethoven played and I ran free?*'

Unfortunately, I'd have to say 'no' once more. In fact, I'm starting to question if I ever had such an experience in the first place. One's memory can play tricks; adding a halcyon hue to past events, and suffusing everyday experiences with a magical tinge which never actually existed. Perhaps I never broke free from my body. Perhaps I was just drunk on the sweet elixir of rebellion; intoxicated by my temporary liberation and high on the discovery of a better life. I don't know. I just don't know. You'll have to decide for yourself.

And now one final question before we part; '*Am I happy?*'

The answer to this one is not so clear. Maybe it's a 'yes', maybe it's a 'no'. Who knows? I mean, what is 'happiness' anyway?

I'm happy a lot of the time. Sometimes I feel an extreme, all-encompassing sort of bliss. At other times I feel a more subtle sort of happiness that can last for many days. I still feel at one with nature. But I also feel detached from human society.

Sometimes I feel sad. Sometimes I feel lonely.

All I know is that I'm happier than I ever was before. I'm vibrating at my natural frequency. I feel calm. My mind is still.

And, for me, that will have to be enough. It's the life I'm settling for. It could be better, but it could be worse. I'm doing things my way, and that feels right.

But this shouldn't be a big revelation; some sort of profound philosophical truth. And nor should it be a lesson. I beg you, dear reader, not to follow in my footsteps. You need to walk your own path through life. You need to work out what is right for you. And no-one, not your parents, not your teachers, and certainly not me, can tell you how to do that. You, dear reader, are your own best teacher. Your own personal experiences will provide you with the best lessons you'll ever receive.

It's like Lao Tzu says; *'The snow goose does not need to bathe to make itself white. Neither do you need to do anything but be yourself... At the centre of your being you have the answer; you know who you are and you know what you want'*.

And with those wise words, we must now bid adieu.

Goodbye dear friend!

Travel your path as best you can.

Be the person you were always meant to be.

'Beep! Beep! Beeeeeeeeeeeeeeep!'

The disciples said to Jesus:

"Tell us how our end will be?"

And Jesus replied:

"Have you already discovered the beginning that you are now asking about the end? For where the beginning is, there the end will be too.

"Blessed is he who will stand at the beginning. He will know the end. And he will not taste death."

THE GOSPEL OF THOMAS

(Verse Fourteen)

ALSO BY JOSS SHELDON...

OCCUPIED

"A unique piece of literary fiction" - **The Examiner**

"Darker than George Orwell's 1984" - **AXS**

"Candid and disquieting" - **Free Tibet**

"Genre-busting" - **Pak Asia Times**

"A must read" - **Buzzfeed**

SOME PEOPLE LIVE UNDER OCCUPATION.

SOME PEOPLE OCCUPY THEMSELVES.

NO ONE IS FREE.

Step into a world which is both magically fictitious and shockingly real, to follow the lives of Tamsin, Ellie, Arun and Charlie; a refugee, native, occupier and economic migrant. Watch them grow up during a halcyon past, everyday present and dystopian future. And be prepared to be amazed.

Inspired by the occupations of Palestine, Kurdistan and Tibet, and by the corporate occupation of the west, 'Occupied' is a haunting glance into a society which is a little too familiar for comfort. It truly is a unique piece of literary fiction...

ALSO BY JOSS SHELDON...

INVOLUTION & EVOLUTION
A RHYMING ANTI-WAR NOVEL

"Flows magnificently across the pages"
"Great, thrilling and enlightening"
"Quick paced and rhythmic"

This is the story of Alfred Freeman, a boy who does everything he can; to serve humankind. He feeds five-thousand youths, salves-saves-and-soothes; and champions the maligned. He helps paralytics to feel fine, turns water into wine; and gives sight to the blind.

When World War One draws near, his nation is plunged into fear; and so Alfred makes a stand. He opposes the war and calls for peace, disobeys the police; and speaks out across the land. He makes speeches, and he preaches; using statements which sound grand.

But the authorities hit back, and launch a potent-attack; which is full of disgust-derision-and-disdain. Alfred is threatened with execution, and suffers from persecution; which leaves him writhing in pain. He struggles to survive, remain alive; keep cool and stay sane.

'Involution & Evolution' is a masterpiece of rhyme, with a message which echoes through time; and will get inside your head. With colourful-characters and poetic-flair, it is a scathing critique of modern-warfare; and all its gory-bloodshed. It's a novel which breaks new ground, is sure to astound; and really must be read.

www.joss-sheldon.com

If you enjoyed this book, please do leave a review on sites like Amazon and Goodreads. Joss Sheldon does not have a professional marketing team behind him – he needs your help to spread the word about his books!!!

Made in the USA
Lexington, KY
26 January 2017